365 Moral Stories

STORICA

PEGASUS

www.pegasusforkids.com

Published by Kuldeep Jain for B. JAIN PUBLISHERS (P) Ltd., D-157, Sector 63, Noida - 201307, U.P

Printed in India

CONTENTS

May

June

July

August

September

October

November

December

The Two Lazy Friends

Best friends, Lisa and Maria, lived together. But both the friends were very lazy.

Each waited for the other to finish the household work but nobody did it. So, their house was always in a mess.

Slowly, rats, mosquitoes and insects gathered in their house. Soon, the friends fell ill.

When the doctor came, he was shocked to see the state of the house. He said, 'You have fallen sick due to your own negligence. If you would have kept your house clean, you could have avoided your illness.'

Lisa and Maria decided to be careful from then on.

Moral: Keep your surroundings clean.

JANUARY 2
The Wise King

Two women came to a wise King's court. The first woman said, 'She stole my baby.'

'This baby is mine!' the second woman shouted.

The King said to a guard, 'Cut the baby into half and give one half to each woman.'

The second woman said, 'I agree.'

The first woman cried, 'Please give my baby to her, but don't harm him!'

The King gave the baby to the first woman and said, 'You are the real mother of the baby for you cannot see him hurt.'

He punished the second woman.

Moral: A mother cannot see her children in trouble.

JANUARY 3
The Teacher and the Boatman

Once, a teacher always boasted about his intelligence.

One day, he went to a boatman and said, 'Take me to the nearby village.'

One the way, the teacher said, 'Boatman, you don't know how to row a boat! Your life is worthless! I am not paying your fare.'

The boatman took the boat in deep waters and rocked it. The teacher fell in the water and began to drown.

The boatman said, 'teacher, you know so much but you don't know how to swim!'

The boatman rescued him but taught him a lesson.

Moral: One should not consider anybody inferior.

JANUARY 4
The Wise Magpie

The birds of the forest decided to choose a King. All the candidates were called to show their talent.

But the judges were pleased to see the peacock spread his beautiful feathers like a fan and dance. So, he was chosen. However, a magpie asked, 'Peacock, can I ask you a question?'

Peacock nodded proudly.

The magpie continued, 'Can you save us from the eagle or the vulture? Only a wise or strong leader could protect us rather than a beautiful one!'

The birds realised their mistake and chose the magpie as their King.

Moral: Character is more important than looks.

JANUARY 5
Tiny Tina

Tina's friends at school called her 'Tiny Tina' as she was a short girl.

One day, she angrily shouted, 'I will be tall very soon.'

Then, she went home and cried all day. Tina's grandmother gave her few pills and said, 'These will help you grow tall.'

Tina took them but instead of getting taller, her body began to itch. Grandmother gave Tina some soothing oil and explained, 'You are a beautiful girl. You will be in trouble if you try to achieve the impossible.'

Tina learnt to be happy with the way she was.

Moral: Be content with what you have.

JANUARY 6
The Farmer's Love for his Daughter

A farmer lived with his wife and daughter. Unfortunately, his wife died in a flood. So, the farmer took his daughter and left his village.

On the way, he was attacked by robbers. They took all his money and saw his little daughter.

She looked like an angel.

They said, 'If you want to live, give us your daughter.'

The farmer cried, 'Kill me before you take my daughter away.'

The robbers thought of their own children and how they would suffer if they died. They gave up stealing and went home.

Moral: Parents love their children more than their own lives.

JANUARY 7
The Naughty Boy

A naughty boy lived in a village. One day, the villagers said to the boy, 'A man lives on the hill top. He sleeps all day. If you wake him, we will give you gold.'

The boy agreed.

On the hill-top, the man was sleeping. The boy tickled him with blades of grass.

The man caught hold of the boy and shouted, 'How dare you wake me up?'

The terrified boy wanted to run. But, the man made him to do all his household chores.

The boy was never naughty again.

Moral: Troublemakers always land in their own troubles.

12

Careless Emma

Emma was a careless girl. She lost many things due to this habit.

One day, Emma's father brought a big doll and said, 'I bring many gifts but you lose everything. If you lose this doll, I will never bring gifts anymore.'

Emma promised but soon forgot about it.

The next day, Emma's father saw the doll lying in the garden. He was very angry and said, 'I have decided never to buy you any toys.'

Emma cried, 'Father, I am really sorry!'

Her father forgave her and from that day, Emma never lost anything.

Moral: One must take care of one's things.

The Wrong Decision

The Sun and the Moon were married a long time back.

One day, they invited the sea for dinner, but the sea said, 'There will not be enough room for me in your house.' But they assured, 'We have a big house. You will not have any problem there.'

As the sea and his family entered the house, the water began to rise.

The Sun and Moon regretted their decision of inviting the sea. They climbed on the roof, but the water kept rising. They finally climbed up to the sky and lived there ever since.

Moral: Think before you act.

JANUARY 10
The Merchant and the Thief

A merchant was travelling with diamonds. Knowing this, a thief followed him. Soon, they were caught in the rain and went to a guest house. As there was only one vacant room, they kept their suitcases there.

When the merchant went out, the thief searched the suitcase.

He found nothing and ran away. After many years, the thief met the merchant and asked, 'That day, I searched your suitcase but I found nothing!'

The merchant said, 'I kept the diamonds in your suitcase when you went out. Luckily, you ran away, leaving your suitcase behind.'

Moral: It is foolish to underestimate your enemy.

JANUARY 11
The Miserly Man

Doctors tried to cure an ill, rich man but did not succeed.

Finally, the man prayed, 'God, save me and I will build a beautiful church.' Soon, his prayers were heard.

But the man broke his promise and bought a tiny idol of Christ. He took it to the church and said, 'God, please accept my gift of thanks.'

That night, he dreamt God saying, 'You will find a bag full of gold on the sea shore.'

The man ran all the way to the sea but there was nothing. The man understood God's lesson and repented.

Moral: Do not make false promises.

JANUARY 12
The Teacher's Fair Decision

Two friends, Dean and Sam had a fierce fight. When their teacher asked about the fight, they blamed each other.

Their teacher said, 'Speak one at a time and let me hear what happened.'

Dean said, 'Sam stole my sweets!'

Sam refused this.

Their teacher said, 'I know Dean is very clever. He can never be fooled. So, Dean will be punished for falsely blaming Sam. However, Sam is very greedy. So, I am sure that he is also guilty. Thus, both will be equally punished for fighting.'

The teacher taught both friends a lesson.

Moral: Be fair in everything you do.

JANUARY 13
God's Advice

A beggar went to the village headman for alms. But, he had gone to meet the King for grants.

The beggar thought, 'The King is definitely richer than the village headman.'

So, he went to the King.

He heard the King praying to God to keep his treasury full.

The beggar thought, 'God must be richer than King.' So, he went before God.

God said, 'Dear child! You should stop begging. Earn your living with hard work and you will always have enough money.'

The beggar took God's advice and worked hard for his living.

Moral: Hard work always pays.

The Foolish Boys

Five boys decided to swim to the other side of a river.

When they reached the other side, a boy said, 'Let us count to see if we all have reached safely.'

He began, 'One, two, three, four…. Oh! Where is our fifth friend?!'

Then, another boy counted and found a boy missing again. He cried out, 'Our fifth friend has drowned.'

All of them started crying. Then, a passer-by made them stand in a row and counted them. He said, 'You all counted others and forgot yourselves.' The boys realised their foolish mistake.

Moral: Do not react before knowing the truth.

The King and the Beggars

A King noticed a beggar rubbing his back against his gates. He asked, 'What are you doing?'

The beggar replied, 'I did not have a bath for days. So, my back is itching.'

The King gave him twenty gold coins.

Later, he saw two beggars rubbing their backs against the gates. He ordered, 'Give them twenty whiplashes!'

They cried, 'The other beggar was rewarded. Why are you punishing us?'

The King replied, 'He could not scratch his own back. But you can scratch each other's back. You are here because of greed.'

The beggars were ashamed.

Moral: Greediness always brings trouble.

JANUARY 16
The Queen and the Gardener

Once, a gardener took some grapes for the Queen. But she was in a bad mood. She tasted a grape and found it sour. She angrily threw the grape at the gardener.

The gardener said, 'God is merciful!'

The Queen asked, 'I have hurt you. Why do you say that God is merciful?'

The gardener said, 'I was going to bring watermelons. But I changed my mind. Imagine what would have happened if you had thrown a watermelon at me. So, I believe that God is merciful.'

The Queen laughed and her anger immediately vanished.

Moral: Whatever happens, it is for good.

JANUARY 17
The Ice cream Seller

Once, a poor boy saw an ice cream cart. The seller cried, 'Strawberry, vanilla, chocolate and butterscotch! Come and take any of them!'

The boy searched his pockets for money but only found a few nuts.

The seller saw this and thought, 'I can fool him and give him an old icecream in exchange of the nuts.' He made the offer and the boy agreed.

After the boy went away, the Seller started eating the nuts. He realised that all the nuts were rotten.

He quickly understood that it was God's way of saying 'Tit for Tat'.

Moral: You reap what you sow.

The Girl and the Wicked Witch

Once, a little girl and her brother played on the hill. A witch lived there. She was angry with the children's noise. She said, 'I will punish you for disturbing my spells.'

The girl said, 'My mother says that if one hurts innocent children, God punishes them severely.'

The witch said, 'God cannot harm me as I have many powers.'

The girl prayed, 'God, save me from the wicked witch.'

When she opened her eyes, she saw a bright light blinding the witch's eyes.

She saw how God punished the wicked and ran down the hill.

Moral: Don't hurt the innocent.

The Kind King

A kind King received an invitation from the wicked neighbouring King. He thought, 'The King will think I am a coward if I don't go. So, I will certainly go.'

The next day, the wicked King ordered his soldiers to put the kind King in prison as soon as he reached.

After a while, his guards informed, 'The neighbouring kingdom has attacked us. Their King cleverly has sent his minister to judge your intentions.'

The kind King had conquered the wicked King's palace by then. He put him in prison and freed many Kings and Princes.

Moral: The wicked will always be punished.

JANUARY 20
The Beautiful Wooden Doll

A poor carpenter's daughter, Marie, saw a rich girl's father buy her a fancy doll.

Marie's mother said, 'Don't be sad! Your father will make you a beautiful doll, soon.'

The next day, Maria's father gave Maria a present. It was a beautiful wooden doll!

Marie was unhappy, for she wanted a fancy doll.

But, she saw her father's hand hurt. Marie understood that her father had hurt his hand while making a doll for her. She, at once, went to him and said, 'Father, this is the most wonderful doll ever! I love it!'

Moral: Appreciate what others do for you.

JANUARY 21
Lima and Mary

Lima had a bad habit. When she did not want to do something, she would say, 'I forgot!'

One day, her friend Mary requested, 'Please bring my notebook tomorrow. Else, the Teacher will scold me.'

Lima was angry with Mary for some reason and did not bring the notebook. When Mary asked, she said, 'I forgot.'

Mary decided to teach her a lesson. She involved others in her plan.

When the entire class went for picnic, everybody left Lima back. Later, when she complained, all her friends shouted, 'We forgot!'

Lima learnt a good lesson.

Moral: Don't make excuses for your work.

19

The Pet Mongoose

Molly and Tom lived on their farm with their daughter, Sara. They had a pet mongoose to keep away snakes.

One day, Molly went to visit her sick aunt and Tom had to leave immediately for the King's court. They left Sara to the Mongoose's care.

The mongoose noticed a huge black snake climb onto her bed. He immediately dragged the snake and killed it.

When Tom and Molly returned, they saw the dead snake.

Then, they saw their daughter play on the bed and understood all that happened. They thanked the mongoose and loved him more.

Moral: Animals love unconditionally.

JANUARY 23

The Miserly Old Woman

A miserly old woman went to buy a coconut. The shopkeeper said, 'Ten copper coins!'

The woman said, 'I will not pay more than five coins!'

Then, she walked five miles and went to another market. The shopkeeper asked for five coins but she wanted to pay three coins.

She walked another three miles to the sea-shore. The coconut Seller asked for three coins but she refused.

She climbed the tree to pick a coconut for free. Suddenly, she slipped and broke her leg.

She paid a thousand coins to the doctor.

Moral: A miser ends up losing all he hoarded.

JANUARY 24
Beautiful Hands

A prince peeped inside a farm house from the keyhole and saw a girl's beautiful hands.

He ordered a diamond ring and announced, 'I will marry the girl in whose ring finger this ring fits.'

Beautiful girls came from different kingdoms but none could wear the ring. The disappointed prince ordered some tea.

A maid came to serve the tea. Suddenly, the prince noticed her beautiful hands. The maid was poor but a beautiful girl.

He put the diamond ring on her finger and it fit her perfectly. The prince married her and they lived happily.

Moral: Look beyond class and caste.

JANUARY 25
The Generous Woman

A King and his army were returning home after a long battle.

As everyone was hungry, the King ordered, 'Soldier, get some fruits.'

The soldier requested a woman, 'Take me to a largest farm.'

She led him to a farm where he picked all the fruits. Then, he asked, 'Is this the largest farm?'

The woman replied, 'No, this is my farm. I could not take you to somebody else's farm knowing that you will pick all that is there.'

The soldier praised her generosity to the King who rewarded her with two huge farms.

Moral: Be generous and kind.

The Lion and the Fox

A brave lion was the king of the forest.

One day, the lion stepped out of his cave and growled loudly. His loud growl echoed from inside the cave.

The lion questioned, 'Who is it? How dare you growl at me?'

But his words echoed back.

The lion was convinced that his enemy wanted to kill him and become the king. He challenged the voice to show himself.

His minister fox said, 'Majesty, the voice is an echo of your voice. Unreal fears can threaten even the brave.'

The foolish lion realised his mistake.

Moral: Always check if your fears are real or unreal.

Polly and her Servant

Polly was sensitive and would cry at the drop of a hat. Any shocking news could be dangerous for her.

One day, her servant wanted to inform that her Mother had died in another town but was worried as she was unwell.

He said, 'All animals in your mother's farm died due to starvation.'

Polly asked, 'Why is mother not feeding them?'

The servant said, 'Kind madam, your mother died a few days back. We could not tell you since you were not well.'

Polly was upset but her life was saved by the clever Servant.

Moral: Be sympathetic and kind towards everybody especially to sensitive people.

The Fisherman and the Sea Goddess

A fisherman caught fish and sold them in the market. But then for a few days he did not get any fish.

So, he decided, 'Either I will catch a fish today or will end my life in the sea.'

Unfortunately, he did not catch anything. Hungry and tired, he fell asleep in his boat.

After sometime, he heard the voice of a woman and woke up.

The sea goddess said, 'Fisherman, I am happy with your hard work.'

She gave him a bag of gold coins to spend the rest of his life happily.

Moral: Hard work will always be rewarded.

Jane and Jo

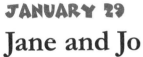

Jo and Jane went to the same school. Jo was pretty but Jane was plain. So, she envied Jo.

One day, Jane forced Jo to steal apples from her neighbour's orchard. Suddenly, Jane heard the guard and jumped the boundary wall.

But, Jo was locked inside. Meanwhile, Jane told the Guard about Jo. But the guard could not find Jo inside.

Later, Jane met Jo. She said, 'Jane, I sneaked out before the guard could find me. You are a dishonest friend. I never want to see you, as you want to harm me.'

Moral: Disloyal people should not be befriended.

JANUARY 30
Clever Matt

A young Matt, once, served an old hermit well. So, he gave him a magic lamp.

When Matt rubbed the lamp, a giant appeared and said, 'I am your slave. Give me work or I'll eat everything around me.'

Matt told the giant to grow crops in his field.

The giant completed the work and came back for more.

Matt thought of a plan. He said, 'Straighten my dog's tail.'

The giant tried for days but could not straighten the tail of the dog. He grew tired and apologised. Matt forgave him and they lived as friends thereafter.

Moral: Quick wit always comes handy.

JANUARY 31
The Blame Game

Once, two friends, Sean and Ron saw a ship full of passengers sink. They watched helplessly from the shore but could not do anything to save them.

Ron guessed, 'Maybe God wanted to kill one bad person aboard, but now He has killed many other innocent people.'

Suddenly, a red ant bit his toe. In anger, he started stamping his feet and crushed many red ants in that area.

Seeing this, Sean said, 'Look at what you did! You killed so many innocent ants to punish the one that bit you!'

Ron realised his mistake and apologised to God for blaming him.

Moral: Do not judge others.

24

The Clever Painter

Old Elise loved her dog a lot.

Once, a painter painted Elise's portrait. However, when Elise showed her dog the portrait, he turned his face and refused to look at it.

Elise shouted, 'You have made a horrible painting. Even my dog refuses to look at it. I will not pay a penny for this.'

The painter requested for another chance. Elise agreed and came three days later. Her dog immediately started licking the portrait.

The clever painter had rubbed some meat on it.

Elise, happily, paid him a lot of money.

Moral: A clever mind can win the day.

The Wise Chief Minister

A King announced, 'Whosoever will solve a riddle will be my chief minister.'

He continued, 'A man has a sheep, a lion and hay. The man has to cross a river and take them in a way that no one will eat the other. Also, only two can go at a time.'

A young man answered, 'First, the man takes the sheep. Then, he takes the lion but brings the sheep with him. Then, he takes the hay and rows back to get the sheep.'

The King appointed him as the chief minister.

Moral: Wisdom has nothing to do with age.

The Dishonest Ministers

The rat kingdom was ruled by a prince and ministers.

One day, the prince brought delicious cheese and said, 'Ministers, distribute this cheese to all the rats. You can keep some for your good work.'

But they became greedy and kept the cheese for themselves while the rest of rats died of hunger.

The prince made some other rats his ministers.

However, the new ministers also became greedy.

An old rat said, 'Shame on you! The prince trusts you. But you only think about yourselves!'

From then, the ministers carried out their duties, honestly.

Moral: Don't be selfish and dishonest.

Pride Comes Before a Fall

An oak tree and an apple tree grew on a roadside.

One day, the apple tree said, 'Old oak, I am very important. Everyone likes my tasty fruits. People nourish me with water. But nobody bothers about you.'

The oak tree said, 'Everything has its own advantages and disadvantages.'

The next day, some boys picked all the apples from the apple tree. They broke many branches and leaves, too. The oak tree said, 'Your juicy apples were advantageous for you but today they invited so much trouble. You are hurt while I stand safe here.'

Moral: One should never be proud.

FEBRUARY 5
Faith in God

A hard-working man earned a lot of wealth but he did not believe in God. His wife prayed to God every day.

One day, the man argued with his wife, 'Who is God? If He is around us, tell Him to prove His presence. I challenge Him to kill me.'

His old father heard him and said, 'Will you kill your son if he asks you to do so? God is also like your father. He can never harm you.'

The man apologised to his wife. After this, he prayed to God every day.

Moral: You must have faith in God.

FEBRUARY 6
The Peasant and the King

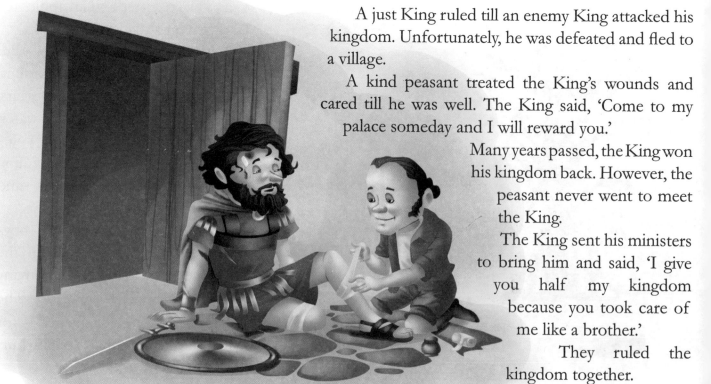

A just King ruled till an enemy King attacked his kingdom. Unfortunately, he was defeated and fled to a village.

A kind peasant treated the King's wounds and cared till he was well. The King said, 'Come to my palace someday and I will reward you.'

Many years passed, the King won his kingdom back. However, the peasant never went to meet the King.

The King sent his ministers to bring him and said, 'I give you half my kingdom because you took care of me like a brother.'

They ruled the kingdom together.

Moral: A kind deed is always repaid.

The Girls in the Park

Two girls had a fight while playing in the park.

The other girls took their sides and soon two groups were formed.

Then, the first group of girls went to a big mean girl and said, 'Come to our park and trouble a group of girls.'

The big mean girl bullied the second group of girls by taking their sweets and toys.

Soon, she started troubling the first group of girls who had invited her. They asked her to leave the park. But, she refused flatly.

Thus, a small fight caused a lot of trouble for all the girls.

Moral: Think before you invite trouble.

The Cunning Wolf

Once, a she-bear gave birth to small cubs. A hungry wolf who was passing by, thought, 'If the she-bear leaves her babies, I can eat them up.'

So, he said, 'How are you feeling today, Mrs. Bear?'

The she-bear replied, 'I'm better, thank you.'

The wolf said, 'Go, take a walk while I take care of your young ones.'

The she-bear replied, 'You came here to hurt my children. I would have been really happy if you actually came to help us. I need to be careful of strangers.'

The disappointed wolf went away.

Moral: Not all sweet words mean well.

29

FEBRUARY 9
The Honest Minister

An honest minister valued all goods in the kingdom fairly and paid the sellers well.

The greedy King thought, 'If he keeps paying everyone so fairly, all my wealth will soon be lost. I will appoint someone who will pay less.'

He selected the first person he saw, who was a foolish man.

Just then, a horse-dealer brought 500 horses for sale. The foolish man valued them at one measure of rice. The horse-dealer asked, 'What is the value of one measure of rice?'

'The whole kingdom, of course!'

The King brought the honest minister back.

Moral: Value just and fair dealings.

FEBRUARY 10
Fox in the Wolf's Skin

A fox and a wolf were good friends. One day, the fox said, 'I just eat fowls. Please teach me how you kill sheep!'

The wolf said, 'You will find the dead body of my brother near the river. Wear his skin and come back.'

Then, the wolf taught the fox to growl and hunt.

Many days after, the fox went to the river, still wearing the dead wolf's skin. She saw some sheep and caught a fat sheep.

Suddenly, she saw a fowl. At once, she left the sheep and pounced on the fowl.

Moral: Natural habits do not change.

The Careful Hare

Once, as a lion was drinking water from the river, a goat came from behind and hit him. The goat's horns injured the Lion.

The angry lion ordered, 'No animal with horns is allowed to live here from now.'

Thus, all the cows, oxen, buffaloes and deer left the forest. A hare was also afraid.

As the hare was leaving, a duck said, 'Do not leave, hare!'

The hare replied, 'Though I do not have horns, my ears are very long. The lion may think that they are horns. So, I am leaving.'

Moral: One must take care of his safety.

Simon and the Bird

Once, Simon saw a bird caught in a net spread by some boys.

The bird was crying for help. Simon freed it and the bird flew away.

A few days later, Simon was eating under a tree. Suddenly, the same bird swooped at his food and took it away.

Simon jumped up to snatch his food back, but lost his balance and fell down. He was angry at the unthankful bird.

However, he saw a poisonous snake crawling down the tree and understood that the snake could have bitten him.

The bird had saved his life.

Moral: Don't misjudge people's intentions.

The Foolish Monk

A monk watched two rams fight. Suddenly, a ram threw the other down at his feet.

The monk thought, 'Ah! This ram understands my value.'

Then, he respectfully folded his hands and bowed before it.

Seeing this, an old man said, 'Don't be foolish. The ram won't think twice before attacking you.'

The monk ignored the man's warning.

Just then, the ram charged towards the monk and knocked him down.

As the monk tried to get up, he sighed, 'I really hope people do not make the same mistake as I did.'

Moral: It is foolishness to ignore wise advice.

The Fussy and the Greedy Birds

A woodcock and a mallard were feeding at a swamp full of snails, frogs and other insects.

The woodcock ate only the best bites but the mallard ate whatever he could find.

The woodcock said, 'Anything and everything is food for you!'

The mallard replied, 'Everyone can eat what he wants! I would rather be greedy than fussy!'

The woodcock haughtily flew away.

Soon, the mallard started eating some garbage. A hook got stuck in his throat and he died.

The woodcock flew straight into a net and was trapped.

Moral: The greedy and haughty people usually suffer in the end.

FEBRUARY 15
The Responsible Girl

Suzy was an obedient and responsible girl.

One day, Suzy's teacher said, 'We are going on a picnic and Suzy will be the monitor. Take care that no one puts their hands or heads out of the bus window. Also, no one should be left behind.'

Suzy replied, 'Yes, madam.'

After picnic, the children boarded the bus.

The teacher noticed Suzy peeping out of the bus window. She said, 'Suzy, I thought you were a responsible girl!'

Suzy said, 'I was checking if anyone is left behind.'

The teacher rewarded Suzy with sweets.

Moral: Be obedient and prompt in all your work.

FEBRUARY 16
The Three Friends and the Hunter

George and his two friends were travelling back to their town when they saw a hunter. He was loading deer meat on his cart.

The first friend said, 'Servant, give me some meat.'

The hunter gave only skin and bone.

The second friend said, 'Brother', give some meat.'

The hunter was touched and he gave a portion of the meat.

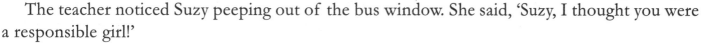

Finally, George asked, 'Dear friend, will you give me a piece of meat.'

Hearing the word 'friend', the emotional hunter offered the whole cart. The three friends and the Hunter became good friends.

Moral: Friendship is the greatest of all relationships.

33

Religions and Customs

A bear was walking through the countryside and saw many fowls drinking water from a pool. After every sip, they would raise their heads to the sky. He asked, 'Why do you look up after you drink water?'

A fowl replied, 'This is an old religious custom. We pay our gratitude to heaven and God for the food and water we receive.'

The bear found it so funny that he laughed aloud.

An old fowl said, 'You are a stranger. But we forgive your rudeness.'

The bear apologised to the fowls.

Moral: We must treat all religions and customs with respect.

Sweet Pears

A King asked his subjects, 'Am I a good ruler?'

Nobody spoke ill of him. So, he thought, 'These people are afraid to tell me the truth!'

Then, the King disguised as a commoner, went to meet a hermit.

Not recognising him, the hermit invited him to his hermitage and offered him sweet pears. The King asked, 'How are these pears so sweet?'

The hermit replied, 'Because our King is both noble and just. If a King is unjust, all the fruits in his kingdom are tasteless.'

The King happily went back.

Moral: The noble and the just are always respected.

The Three Brothers and the Penny

Al, Albert and Alvin found a penny while roaming in a park. They decided to buy something to eat and share it equally.

Al said, 'I want to eat something sweet!'

Albert said, 'No! I want to eat something healthy.'

Alvin said, 'No! I want to drink something.'

An old man heard them fighting. He took the penny and bought a bunch of grapes with it.

He said, 'Al, these grapes are sweet. Albert, these fruits are healthy and Alvin, they are juicy, so they will quench your thirst!'

The brothers thanked the old man and enjoyed the grapes.

Moral: Use your common sense wisely.

Silly Kathy

Kathy was a silly girl. Every day, she went to collect wood from the forest. One such day, she fell asleep under a tree.

When Kathy woke up, it was very dark. As she walked home, she reached a lake.

'Let me drink some water!' thought Kathy. However, she could not see her reflection in the water.

Kathy thought she had become invisible. She was happy with her new power and decided to test it.

Kathy walked to a monkey fearlessly and teased him. The monkey scratched her all over!

Moral: It is foolish to think that one is all powerful.

Teachers Deserve Respect

A thief entered the King's orchard and climbed the trees to fill his bag with fruits.

Then, he saw the King with an old monk, sitting under a tree. The monk sat on the ground while the King sat on a chair.

The thief wondered, 'Our King does not respect his teacher. No wonder our kingdom is not flourishing!'

The thief slid down the tree and said, 'Majesty, your teacher deserves respect. Proper respect will give you great rewards.'

The King understood and regretted his actions. He rewarded the thief and apologised to his teacher.

Moral: One's teacher is always superior.

Laziness Cost Jane her Job

Lazy Jane saw a princess fall from her horse and nursed her wounds.

The princess said, 'Jane, will you work for me? Come to my palace before sunset.'

Jane went home and said, 'Give me lunch, mother. Then I will go.'

After lunch, Jane took a nap. Then, she went towards the palace. She felt tired, so, sat under a tree to rest.

When Jane reached the palace, it was already sunset. The palace doors were shut.

Jane thought, 'I lost the princess's offer because of laziness! I will never be lazy again!'

Moral: Due to laziness, you can lose opportunities.

FEBRUARY 23
The Wicked Dream Interpreter

A King called his ministers, one day, and said, 'Last night, I heard wailing sounds in my dreams!'

The King's dream interpreter thought, 'This is a good chance to make money.'

He said, 'Majesty, your life is in danger. You must sacrifice animals.'

The frightened King agreed.

As the King was about to sacrifice animals, a hermit stopped him. He said, 'The voices in your dream will bring no harm. Instead, killing these animals will trouble you all your life.'

The King thanked the hermit. He freed the animals and punished his dream interpreter.

Moral: Do not harm innocent animals.

FEBRUARY 24
Lizzy and her Friends

Lizzy was adorable but she was bossy and would always order her friends.

One evening, Lizzy went to the park. Her friends were playing doctor and patients.

Lizzy demanded, 'I want to play teacher. Jenna, you will be the student. Lea will be the peon and Belle will be the bus driver.'

Lizzy's friends said, 'No! All of us want to play doctor!'

Lizzy ran home in tears. Her mother said, 'Lizzy, you should not force them to play the games of your choice or you won't have any friends.'

Lizzy was never bossy again.

Moral: Bullies should not be tolerated.

Beth and the Blue Fairy

Once, the blue fairy visited young Beth and saw her helping everyone. The blue fairy decided to test her and bewitched her mirror.

When Beth saw her reflection, she looked very frightening. Her pretty face was large and swollen, her blue eyes were red and her nose looked like witch'.

The mirror said, 'Your face shall be pretty again, only if you will be cruel to everyone.'

Beth said, 'No! I will not hurt anyone!'

Suddenly, the mirror shattered. The blue fairy appeared and said, 'Beth, you passed my test!' She gave Beth healing powers.

Moral: Looks don't matter, kindness does.

The Three Clever Mice

Some mice lived in an old woman's house.

One day, they saw a piece of cheese in a little room. They decided to go inside. But three mice didn't want to go. The others asked them, 'Why are you not coming with us?'

They replied, 'There is one door in the room. If it closes, we all will be trapped.'

When the mice pounced on the cheese, the door closed.

The room was a trap set by the old woman. The wise three mice ran quickly to their holes.

It is silly to be greedy and put ourselves in trouble.

Sally and the Saplings

Poor Sally worked as a maid. One day, her mistress gave her some saplings.

Sally thought, 'I should plant them soon, so that everyone can enjoy them.'

Thus, she planted them by her hut and watered them.

Soon, plenty of flowers bloomed around her hut. She invited children to look at them and old people to eat their fruit.

One day, Sally saw that the fruits had turned into jewels! A fairy appeared and said, 'This is your reward for being selfless!'

Sally sold the jewels and was never poor again.

Moral: Be selfless and think of everyone around you.

The Monkey and the Parrot

The King's children loved their pet parrot a lot.

One day, the King was presented a monkey. The King loved the monkey's tricks. So, the proud monkey said, 'Silly parrot, I am smarter than you. Soon, I will make the King throw you out of the palace.'

The parrot replied, 'I'm sure things will be normal soon.'

After a few days, the King introduced the monkey to his children. However, they were frightened and began to cry. So, the King ordered, 'Drive this monkey away.'

Thus, the proud monkey was sent away. The parrot remained everyone's favourite.

Moral: Old is Gold.

Valuable Advice

A rich man gave his entire wealth to his sons and went on a pilgrimage. A cunning merchant advised them wrongly and ran away with their money.

When the man returned, his friends narrated the tale of his sons' downfall.

But the man did not scold them. Rather, he said, 'Work hard and you will be rich again.'

The surprised sons asked, 'Father, are you not angry with us?'

The man replied, 'If wealth is lost, nothing is lost. If health is lost, something is lost. But if character is lost, everything is lost.'

Moral: Money is not everything in one's life.

The Prince and the Priest's Son

A prince and a priest's son were great friends.

After the King's death, the prince ascended the throne. The priest's son, however, did not have any fascination for worldly things.

He went away and lived in the forest, praying to God.

After the priest's death, the King went to bring his friend back. But he said, 'I will not give up chosen path. But if you ever need my advice, you may come to me.'

The King respected him all the more and went to meet him often.

Moral: A true friend will guide you towards the right path.

The Wise Lion and the Foolish Hare

A hare was sleeping under a tree. Suddenly, a ripe fruit fell to the ground, making a loud noise. The frightened hare thought, 'This is the sound of a crack in the earth's surface. The universe is coming to an end!'

He screamed, 'Run! Save yourselves! The earth's surface is cracking.'

The animals panicked and ran. Then, the lion King said, 'Hare, take us to that place.'

When the lion saw the fallen fruit, he said, 'The sound was only that of a fruit falling!' The hare was embarrassed.

Moral: Look for the reason behind something first, instead of being scared.

Overconfidence Can Kill

A lion met a jackal near the lake. The frightened jackal said, 'Don't kill me. I will be your servant.' The lion took him home and fed him daily.

Once, the jackal boasted, 'Today, I will kill an elephant for you.' The lion warned, 'You can't kill an elephant as it is big and strong.'

However, the jackal did not listen and sprang at an elephant. The elephant caught him in his trunk and crushed him. Within minutes, the Jackal died.

The lion saw the dead jackal and thought, 'He is dead because of his own pride!'

Moral: Don't be overconfident.

The Horse's Pride

Two friends were going to the market to sell their goods. Their horses were laden with bags.

The first horse was full of pride because it was carrying precious gems.

The other horse was calm. It was carrying iron tools.

As they were passing through a forest, some thieves stopped them. The two friends ran away, leaving their horses behind.

As the thieves found nothing valuable, they let the second horse go. The thieves killed the first horse who was standing stiff with pride and took away the gems.

Moral: There is no use of pride when it can't save one's life.

MARCH 6
Hard Work Pays

Young Bonnie disliked working hard and was lazy.

Her mother decided to teach her a lesson. She said, 'Bonnie, go to the end of the rainbow. You will find treasure, there.'

Bonnie ran towards the rainbow, but she did not know which end to go. She went to the left end. There was nothing there.

Angrily, Bonnie began walking towards the right end. She reached there, feeling tired.

Her mother said, 'I wanted you to know that without hard work, you will be empty-handed always.'

Bonnie understood that treasure comes through hard work.

Moral: Work hard and you will be rewarded.

MARCH 7
The Horse Thief

Brian was resting under a tree while his horse grazed nearby. Soon, he fell asleep.

When Brian woke up, his horse was missing. He looked everywhere but his horse was nowhere.

Brian went to the nearby village and waved a stick, shouting, 'Who stole my horse? I will teach the thief a lesson like I did last time!'

The frightened thief came there and said, 'Here is your horse. But what did you do the last time, when your horse was stolen?'

Brian said, 'Nothing! I bought a new horse!'

Moral: Wit and humour can help you get out of difficulties.

The Foolish Sisters

A fairy granted three wishes to Molly and Mia for their hard work. They said, 'Thank you, fairy! We'll ask for wishes soon.'

That night, they sat thinking about the three wishes. Suddenly, Molly said, 'I wish, we had chicken to eat.'

A chicken appeared on their plate.

Mia scolded, 'Foolish girl, you have wasted a wish! I hope this chicken sticks to your nose!'

The chicken flew and stuck to Molly's nose. She said, 'I wish to be free of this chicken.' The chicken vanished.

All three wishes were wasted because of their foolishness.

Moral: Don't speak without thinking.

The Magical Bird and the Kind King

A bird catcher heard about a magical bird. When she sang, shiny pearls fell from her beak.

The bird catcher caught the magical bird. He kept her in a golden cage and fed it well but the bird did not sing at all.

The bird catcher was fed up and gifted her to the King.

At once, the kind King freed the Bird. The bird was so happy that she sang and a shower of pearls fell on the King.

From that day, the magical bird visited the King and sang for him.

Moral: An act of kindness brings great rewards.

Ella and the Poor Girl

Ella saw a poor girl standing outside her school, everyday. She wanted to talk to the girl but the girl ran away.

One evening, Ella saw the girl again. She asked her what she was doing there. The girl said, 'I live here with my ill mother. I have no money to buy her medicine.'

Ella's parents were kind. They took the girl's mother to a hospital. Then, they took the girl home with them.

When the girl's mother was well, she started working.

Ella and the girl went to school together.

Moral: Help the needy as much as you can.

Brave Girl Janie

Janie went to the forest with her father to collect wood and was lost.

Soon, it was dark. As Janie was walking, she met a frightening man. Holding a knife in his hand, he said, 'Give me whatever you have!'

Janie gave him her ring. Then he said, 'Give me your axe, too!'

Janie threw the axe at the man's hand. When the knife fell, Janie, at once, picked it up.

Just then, Janie's father came and hit the man with a stick. The man ran away and Janie went home with her father.

Moral: Stand up against the wicked, bravely.

The Old Woman and the Mean Lady

A poor old woman was generous and would share her food with the needy.

One day, she went a rich mean lady's house. The mean lady rudely said, 'I can't give anything!'

The old woman said, 'Please help me, for I am poor.'

So, the mean lady angrily gave her some stale food.

As the old woman was about to eat, a little boy said, 'I am hungry.'

The old woman gave all the food to the boy. After eating the food, the boy fell terribly sick. The little boy was the mean lady's son.

Moral: What goes around, comes around.

True Love and Orchids

Bethany dearly loved Luke, who was her neighbour. However, Luke was in love with beautiful Anna.

Once, Anna said, 'I want the orchids from the forest.' Luke readily agreed. But, a wild boar hurt him, badly.

Bethany took good care of Luke. Soon, he was better and thanked her.

When Luke met Anna, she asked, 'Did you bring the orchids?' Luke was amazed that Anna did not care about him and just wanted orchids.

He went to Bethany and said, 'Your love is selfless. It has made me love you, too.' Soon, they were happily married.

Moral: True love is selfless.

MARCH 14
The Foolish Tail

A snake lived in the valley.

One day, his tail fought with his head, 'Don't you feel bad that you make me follow you?'

The head replied, 'I lead you because I have eyes and brain, while you do not.'

The tail said, 'Please, let me lead you for a few days. It is only fair.'

Finally, the head agreed.

The tail began to lead and the snake started moving backwards. Soon, the snake fell from the edge of the valley and was wounded.

Then onwards, the tail did not want to lead the head.

Moral: Think twice before you act.

MARCH 15
The Queen of Flowers

The Queen of flowers disguised herself as a common woman and visited a kingdom for a flower festival.

Everyone looked for the source of a divine fragrance. Then, they saw the woman wearing a ring of flowers.

The woman said, 'One needs to be honest and noble to wear these magical flowers.'

A wicked wizard lied, 'I have all the qualities you speak of.'

But, as he held it, his head ached badly. He cried, giving back the ring, 'I lied! Forgive me!'

The woman returned to heaven, saying, 'Change your wicked ways now.'

Moral: Liars are always caught.

MARCH 16
The Sorcerer and the Princess

A sorcerer visited a King and was charmed by the princess' beauty.

The King had invited the sorcerer for dinner. The sorcerer mixed a magic potion in the King's drink. The King fell into deep sleep.

Then, the sorcerer took the princess away to his castle. On the way, the princess threw away her ornaments, one-by-one.

Next morning, the King learnt that his daughter was gone! He left with his army and found the ornaments on the way. He reached the sorcerer's castle and punished him for his deeds. Thus, the princess was saved.

Moral: Evil deeds have bad endings.

MARCH 17
A Clever Trick

A lion saw a boar but let him go for he was in a hurry. However, the boar thought, 'The lion is afraid of me.' He challenged the lion, 'Let us fight!'

The lion replied, 'Not today. Come back next week.'

The boar's friends said, 'You shouldn't have challenged the Lion.'

The frightened boar asked his friends for advice. They replied, 'Roll in a dunghill. When the lion smells you, he will let you go.'

On the day of the fight, the lion said, 'You stink! I won't eat you. You are free!'

Moral: A little common sense helps in difficulties.

The King's Nightingale

A King kept a nightingale in a cage and fed him good food.

However, he was sad. He thought the birds outside had wonderful and happy lives.

One day, his master forgot to latch the cage door. The nightingale flew straight out of the window to a large shady tree.

'Ah! This is wonderful,' he cried.

However, the nightingale did not know how to get food. Also, he could not sleep in the open.

Then, a thunderstorm broke out. The nightingale felt cold and cried out, 'I wish I was in my cage!'

Moral: The grass is greener on the other side.

The Beautiful Robe

Catalina was once watching the King's procession. The Queen was dressed in beautiful robes.

Catalina wondered how she could get such a robe. Then, she began working in the palace and served the Queen well. The Queen presented her with a beautiful robe.

On her way home, Catalina saw a hermit shivering and gave him her robe.

The hermit said, 'I bless you. Go bathe in the river. It will make you most beautiful.'

Catalina did as the hermit said and saw her beautiful reflection. Then, a prince was passing by. He fell in love and married her.

Moral: A kind act can bring a blessing in disguise.

MARCH 20
Memories

A man was selling off his parent's old home.

His mother was very sad, she did not want to leave her home but her son would not agree.

The man was emptying all rooms. He found an old photo album in a room. He showed it to his mother.

His mother said, 'Son, see how your father and I kept all your growing up memories in this album. We treasured every picture. And you can't treasure a house built by your father!'

The man was ashamed. He hugged his mother and said, 'I won't sell the house!'

Moral: Treasure old memories.

MARCH 21
A Great Monk

A monk asked his father, 'What must I do to become a great monk?' Father replied, 'You must only think of and pray to God.'

The monk spent long hours in the forest, reciting God's name. He went hungry many times, but would think of God and carry on. His devotion was so sincere that the angels decided to test him.

They sent a dancer to distract the monk. She danced and sang but he was quiet, with his eyes closed.

The angels were pleased and said, 'You are indeed a great monk!'

Moral: Patience and devotion will eventually pay off.

The Fox and the Mole

A hungry fox sat under a tree, waiting for a prey to pass by. Just then, she saw a mole who lived in a hole under the tree.

The fox said, 'God is unkind to you. You live underground and cannot enjoy the sun.'

The mole said, 'I am very thankful to God for his gifts.'

The fox laughed, 'God does not care for creatures like you.'

He said, 'God loves

me. He protects those who have faith in Him.'

Suddenly, the mole ran inside his hole. The next moment, a hunter came and shot the fox.

Moral: Do not put others down because God treats everyone equally.

The Merchant and the Mermaid

A kind merchant always fed the poor. Soon, his money ran out. He thought, 'I must go to the enchanted city and bring more gold.'

While sailing, he stopped at an island and met an old man. He gave him food and water.

Soon, a storm arose and the ship sank. When he was drowning, a mermaid rescued him.

She said, 'I am the old man you were so kind to. What do you want?'

The merchant said, 'Gold to provide for the poor.'

She gave him a ship and lots of gold.

Moral: Help the poor and God will help you.

The Happy Hen

A hen was crackling on a farm, near a swamp. A frog called out, 'Mrs. Hen, please be quiet.'

The hen stopped at once and looked up at the frog in surprise. The frog continued, 'Why are you making such a racket?'

The hen asked, 'Can't you see I have laid an egg?' 'Oh, such a lot of noise over one egg!' said the frog.

'I never complain when you croak at night. Today, I am singing because I have done something good, though it may be small.' said the hen.

Moral: You must learn to share the happiness of others.

The Greedy Fisherman

A fisherman found a crocodile's egg on the riverbank. It was a magical egg that took whatever shape it wished.

Soon, the egg hatched. It had a human body with scaly crocodile skin. His wife cared for it like it was her own child.

The crocodile said, 'If I enter a river, I will lose my human body. So, make a pond here and you will be rich.'

The rich fisherman greedily thought, 'If my son comes to the river, I will catch more fish!'

When the crocodile saw the river, he slipped away.

Moral: Greed will only make you lose everything.

Liars will Certainly be Caught

A naughty rabbit was very troublesome.

One day, he shouted, 'Sister! I smell something odd!'

His sister knew her little brother well; so she did not react. He screamed again, 'Sister! Do help! I can hear the noise of a hundred explosions!'

The sister still did not say anything. The rabbit stopped near the mouth of the burrow and shouted, 'Oh! What is it that I am seeing? It's the fire from a huge furnace!'

The sister replied, 'Do not tell such a lie, for if there was a fire, we would be burning, too.'

Moral: Don't lie to attract attention.

The Miser and the Pixies

Once, a friend gifted some fish to miser Lance. He thought, 'I shall not share it but will cook it in the forest.'

But the smell of the dish spread and the pixies were tempted. They asked, 'Please give us some fish.'

Lance replied, 'Sorry! This dish is for me only.'

The pixies said, 'Just like taking so much trouble to cook the fish so far away in the forest just to eat it by yourself, there is no point in storing money if you cannot enjoy it.'

Lance understood and thanked them.

Moral: Learn to share as it brings joy.

The Captain and the Sailors

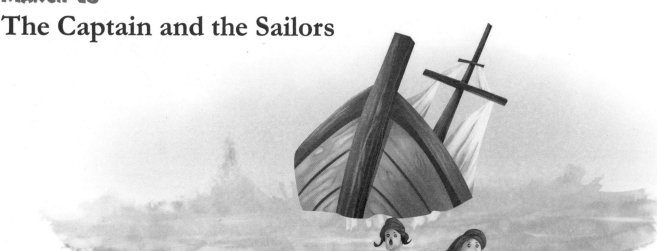

A ship was loaded with heavy iron and wood. So, the sailors were unable to turn the ship.

The captain said, 'Throw the extra iron and wood into the sea. Then the ship will start moving faster.'

The sailors did as they were told.

Suddenly, a storm rose. The waves started rising high. The light ship moved from one side to the other.

Soon, the ship completely tilted to one side and all the sailors drowned. If the captain had kept the extra weight on the ship, the ship would have not drowned.

Moral: All things have their own importance.

The Prince Learns a Lesson

A prince and a minister's son, Simon, grew up together.

One day, the prince said, 'Simon, father is not passing on the throne to me. So, I will kill him.'

Simon said, 'Money and power will come. But if you kill your father, he won't come back.'

However, the prince spoke to some soldiers. They told the King about the prince's plans.

The King said, 'You don't have to kill me, Son. I give you my kingdom.' Saying this, tears ran down his eyes.

The prince was ashamed and apologised to his father.

Moral: Guide your friends in the right direction.

MARCH 30
The Greedy Cat

Once, a cat was very sad. She wanted to eat fish and meat. But her poor master could not afford that.

One day, the cat saw a dovecote. A few chicks had hatched out of the eggs. The cat thought, 'How tasty they would be to eat!'

She slowly went to catch the chicks. The owner, who was watching, trapped the cat with his net and beat her up.

When the cat's master saw her, he cried, 'My poor cat! If only you were satisfied with the food I gave you, you would be safe.'

Moral: Be satisfied with what you have.

MARCH 31
Tasty Nuts

Bob's mother kept a big jar of hazel nuts for him.

When Bob returned from school, he excitedly put his hand into the jar and grabbed a handful.

However, his hand got stuck in the jar!

Bob tried to free his hand many times, but failed. Tears rolled down his cheeks. He thought, 'Oh, I want to eat these tasty nuts!'

His gardener looked through the window and said, 'Bob, just let go of some of the nuts! Then your hand will easily slip out!'

Bob obeyed and his hand slipped out.

Moral: Take only as much as you can hold.

55

Don't Blame Others

A hungry fox was chasing a small dog. The dog ran fast and jumped over a thorny hedge. The fox also tried to jump, but he fell on a bramble bush. He was scratched badly by the thorny bramble.

The fox blamed the thorny bramble and said, 'I held on to you to save myself from falling and you hurt me so badly.'

The thorny bramble replied, 'With so many thorns, how could you even think of holding on to me without getting hurt? Do not blame someone else for your foolish actions.'

Moral: Blaming others for your mistakes is wrong.

Keep Away From Bad Habits

Vice and Fortune were arguing about their power.

Vice said, 'I am all the bad habits a man can have.'

Fortune said, 'I am a man's fate. If a good man's luck is bad, he can easily become evil.'

Vice laughingly narrated, 'A man had everything because of good luck. Gambling was his only vice and he lost all his riches. If a man's luck is good but he has bad habits, he cannot be happy.'

Fortune understood that Vice was more dangerous for mankind.

Moral: It is difficult to get rid of bad habits.

Witty Fox

Once, a lion invited an ass to his house. As soon as he entered the lion's cave, the lion caught him. The lion told his minister, 'Fox, watch the ass. If you touch him, I shall be angry.'

The fox waited but grew hungry. As the lion was nowhere in sight, he ate the ass's brain. The lion returned and roared, 'Fox, where is the ass's brain?'

The fox quickly said, 'Brain? The ass had none. Or he wouldn't have walked into your trap so easily.' The lion laughed and the fox was saved.

Moral: Quick wit always helps in tricky situations.

Don't Believe in Rumours

One day, a King heard about the friendship of a cow and lioness and decided to visit them.

Meanwhile, a sly jackal thought, 'I'll make these friends fight with each other. Then, I shall eat them!'

So, the jackal started creating ill will between them. The cow and the lioness believed him.

One day, the cow heard a rumour and argued with the lioness. They fought bitterly and killed each other.

When the King came to see the friends, they were dead! The King sighed, 'Rumours can ruin any friendship.'

Moral: Always believe what you see and hear, not in rumours.

A Father's Love

Once, a farmer brought up his son all alone. Years passed and the son grew into a bright young boy.

The farmer had become old. He constantly asked his son to get food and water. This irritated his son greatly.

One day, the son said angrily, 'Old man, I am fed up. I can't take care of you anymore.'

The farmer said, 'Son, I nurtured you since you were a baby. I fed you before I ate. I never complained.'

The son apologised to his father and took great care of him.

Moral: Look after your parents when they are old.

Clever Jester

Once, a wise and just King ruled a kingdom. King's royal jester Tucan was very clever. He cracked funny jokes and also helped the King in the court.

Often, Tucan would even crack jokes at the King!

One day, the King felt insulted at one of Tucan's jokes and said, 'Guards, seize this man! He will be hanged tomorrow!'

When Tucan was to be hanged, the King asked, 'What is your last wish?' Clever Tucan replied, 'Majesty, I wish to die of old age.'

The King began laughing at Tucan's wit and forgave him.

Moral: Humour can save one from difficulties.

APRIL 7
Trust your Abilities

A fox asked a cat, 'How many tricks do you know?'

The cat replied, 'I know only one trick. When the dogs chase me, I know how to climb trees and escape.'

The fox said, 'I will show you my bagful of tricks.'

Just then, the cat heard the hunters and their dogs. The fox said, 'Don't be afraid! I will teach you a good trick.' But the cat jumped on the tree.

The dogs chased the fox and caught him.

The cat shouted, 'Fox! All the tricks put together will not save you now!'

Moral: Being boastful does not help in times of trouble.

APRIL 8
The Proud Goose

A proud goose always found faults in others. He said, 'Man is so proud of himself. He always talks bad about others and thinks he is superior.'

Then, he said, 'The peacock always shows his colourful feathers and dances.'

One day, the goose saw beautiful swans swimming in the stream.

The goose said, 'These swans are imitating me. Once, I start swimming, they will realise their fault.'

When the goose started swimming, the swans started laughing. They said, 'You are too proud to see the beauty of other animals. We should respect everyone around us.'

Moral: Don't be too proud of yourself.

APRIL 9
Queen Ella

Queen Ella was known for her justice.

Once, she went to a riverside and ordered her ministers to build a palace, there.

The ministers said, 'Majesty, a poor woman's house is in the place where the palace is to be built. It will ruin the beauty of the palace.'

The Queen said, 'She will be given a better place to live in.'

But the old woman begged, 'I cannot leave my house. It is my dead husband's home.'

The Queen understood the old woman's sentiments and let her house remain.

Moral: Be compassionate towards the poor and the needy.

APRIL 10
The Noble King

A noble King once punished his wicked minister and sent him away.

The wicked minister wanted revenge. So he helped the neighbouring King to defeat and capture the noble King.

However, the noble King prayed to God. Immediately, his shackles became loose and he was able to escape. At the same time, a searing pain ran down the wicked minister's body.

A wise man said, 'The King is noble and innocent. You are suffering because you tortured him.'

The neighbouring King returned the noble King's kingdom and punished the minister.

Moral: The wicked always get punished for their deeds.

61

Be Satisfied with What you Have

During winter, a horse's stable became cold and he ate dry plants and straw.

He sighed, 'I wish spring comes soon, then I'll eat fresh grass.'

In spring, he had to carry heavy weights and thought, 'I wish summer comes soon and I'll have less work.'

In hot summer, it was even more difficult to work. He waited for autumn.

In autumn, the horse had to work as people stored food. He thought, 'I hated winter last year, now I am eagerly waiting for winter, so I can rest.'

Moral: Happy people are those who are content with what they have.

Everyone is Troubled

Long ago, each man was created with a sack for his troubles.

Once, God saw that men complained about being more troubled than the other.

God angrily said, 'You all think that you are more troubled than the other and your sack of troubles is bigger. So, just exchange your sack with your neighbours.'

Everyone joyfully turned to their neighbours. However, strangely, they saw that the neighbours' sacks were bigger than theirs!

They said, 'Father, we are fine with our own troubles. Others are more troubled than us.' Then, they stopped complaining.

Moral: Solve your problems rather than comparing them with others.

Bad Company brings Bad Habits

Once, a dog decided to travel. His mother advised him, 'Never be friendly with bad people because keeping bad company can spoil your character.'

Soon, the dog felt thirsty and went to the river.

A cunning crocodile called, 'Be my friend.'

The dog and the crocodile became friends.

One day, the crocodile said, 'Friend, please bring a lamb here. We can both eat it.' The dog went to a nearby farm. As he tried to lure the lamb, the farmer hit him with a stick.

The poor Dog said, 'Oh! My mother was so right.'

Moral: Keep away from bad company.

The Greedy Hawker and the Golden Bowl

An old woman rarely used a golden bowl, so it was completely covered with dirt. Also, she never knew that it was made of gold.

She went to a hawker and wanted a pan in exchange for the bowl. The greedy hawker realised that it was gold. He said, 'It's worth just a small pot.'

The old woman went to another hawker. This honest man gave 500 pieces of silver and many goods.

Later, the greedy hawker visited the woman again. She scolded him, 'You lied to me. I sold it to an honest person.'

Moral: Never cheat or fool anyone.

Don't Share Secrets

A King ruled over his kingdom.

One day, his step-son went to the King's servant and said, 'The King wants to kill me. Promise to save my life!'

The servant readily promised.

Soon, the King asked the servant to poison the prince.

The servant warned the prince, at once.

A few days later, the King fell ill and died. The prince became the new King and said, 'Servant, the old King trusted you. But, you told me his secret. You will never keep my secrets. Go away.'

Moral: If someone trusts you with their secret, don't tell it to anyone.

Check Twice than Checking Only once

Once, a she-goat said to her son, 'I am going out. Do not open the door to anyone but me.'

The kid said, 'Mother, how will I know that it is you on the door?'

She said, 'Open the door only when I call out, 'Beware of the Wolf'.'

A cunning wolf heard the password. He shouted after a while, 'Beware of the Wolf.'

The kid thought, 'Should I open the door or check again?'

Then, he said, 'Show me your white paw.'

The wolf had brown, furry paws and left the house.

Moral: It is always better to check your doubts, twice.

The King and the Elephant

Once, a thorn pierced an elephant's foot. He cried out in pain!

A King was hunting nearby. He took out the thorn and asked the elephant to live in the palace.

The elephant agreed and helped the King fight battles.

After a few years, the King died.

An enemy King declared a battle.

The Queen went to the elephant and said, 'Your master is dead. My son is very young. He can't fight a battle. Please, win the kingdom back for him.'

The elephant led the army and defeated the enemy King.

Moral: A small kind deed can bring great returns.

Be Considerate towards Others

A cook had a hen and a pet parrot.

The hen knew that the cook could cook her. She hid in the kitchen all day.

One day, the cook tried to bring the hen to the cooking stove. However, she jumped up on a cupboard.

The parrot said, 'Hen, go to the cook, as I do when he calls me.'

The poor hen replied, 'The cook's call for me is a sign of death. To you, it is not a matter of worry, though. Be thoughtful towards others' situation.'

The parrot apologised to the hen.

Moral: Be sympathetic towards others' problems.

APRIL 19
Stubbornness Brings Pain

A young woman was always sad because she had no children. A few months later, a fairy appeared and said, 'What do you want, my child?'

'I want a son!' the woman said.

The fairy said, 'I can grant you a daughter.'

'I want a son!' said the woman.

The fairy said, 'I will grant you a son, but your stubbornness will bring you pain.'

Soon, the woman had a son. But the boy was disobedient and dishonest. He earned bad name for her. The woman realised how wrong she was.

Moral: Listen to the advice given by the wise people.

APRIL 20
Seek Help from Understanding People

Mike rented a cottage with a garden. He grew different kinds of fruits, vegetables and flowers.

But a hare destroyed Mike's plants.

Mike said to his landlord, 'There is a hare in your garden that spoils all my plants.'

The landlord ordered hunters and dogs to hunt down the hare.

The hare saw the dogs and jumped from one place to another. The dogs, too, followed him.

The garden was completely destroyed!

Mike cried, 'I was a fool to have taken your help! I should have asked help from those who understood the problem well.'

Moral: Don't ask help from inconsiderate people.

A Boastful Owl

An eagle often ate up owl's children.

One day, the eagle said, 'We are neighbours, and we should become friends!'

The owl replied, 'Promise that you will stop eating my children. They are the ones with pretty eyes.'

The eagle promised.

A few days later, the eagle saw owl's children. But she thought, 'These are ugly children with large yellow eyes. They cannot be the owl's children.'

The eagle ate them. The owl was angry.

The eagle said, 'You said that your children are beautiful. I ate ugly children.' The owl stopped boasting.

Moral: Boasting about oneself only brings trouble.

Love your True Self

God created man as his best work.

When animals saw man, they started imitating him.

The lion took on man's strength and dynamism. The fox imitated man's cleverness. The dog gained man's friendly nature. The parrot started talking in the human tongue.

The ape controlled his hands. The cat adopted man's elegant walk, sharp looks and serious nature.

But Destiny said, 'You all have gained manly qualities but you should not be unhappy with their original selves.'

Destiny taught them to inculcate the qualities of others, but not to dislike their true self.

Moral: Everyone has unique qualities in them.

The Two Doctors

An old man fell ill and called for a doctor.

Soon, the old man sent for another doctor.

The second doctor gave a different treatment from what was advised by the first doctor.

The two doctors continued treating the old man for two different sicknesses.

One day, the doctors met by chance at the old man's bedside and started arguing.

The old man woke up and said, 'Please stop arguing. You did not ask me the problem just prescribed medicines. I have been well for ten days without taking either of your medicines.'

Moral: A doctor should listen well to his patients.

The Bully

A proud crow felt that all the animals should obey her.

One day, the crow saw some sheep grazing. He arrogantly said to a sheep, 'I am tired of flying. You will carry me on your back today.'

The poor sheep carried the crow around.

Soon, she was tired and said, 'If you had treated a dog this way, he would have bitten you.'

The crow said, 'I only order around those who are weak. I know exactly who to bully and who to flatter.'

The Sheep never talked to the crow again.

Moral: Cunning creatures should be treated sternly and not feared.

68

Think before Blaming Others

A miser was counting his money.

A magpie flew into his house and took one of his gold coins, slyly. Then, he hid himself in a hole in the wall.

As the miser looked for his missing gold coin, he found the magpie with it.

The miser said, 'Thief! You stole my gold coin. You did not ask me if you could borrow it.'

The magpie replied, 'You made this money by fooling people and lying to them. You are calling me a thief! I only hid the gold coin here.'

Moral: Learn to share your things with others.

Having many Friends means No Good Friends

A hare heard the hounds coming to catch her. So, the hare went to the horse for help. The horse said, 'I have to do some work for my master.'

The hare asked the bull and he replied, 'I have a meeting with a friend.'

The lamb said, 'I can't help you because hounds eat lambs also.'

Finally, the hare asked the calf for help. The calf said, 'How can I help you when the others cannot help you?'

The hounds had come very close. The hare quickly ran and saved herself.

Moral: Trust your own abilities. Don't expect from others.

APRIL 27
Valuable Words

A gardener worked hard all day.

At night, he lay under a tree and heard a nightingale sing beautifully. Her song was so sweet that he forgot his aching body and felt peaceful.

He put the nightingale in a cage.

The nightingale said, 'Free me, and I will tell you three very valuable things.'

When the gardener set the nightingale free, she flew to a high branch and said, 'Never take a prisoner's promise seriously. Be happy with what you have. Don't be sad about what is lost.'

Then, the nightingale flew away.

Moral: Do not harm animals or birds.

APRIL 28
The Brave Horse

A dog was roaming in the jungle. Just then, he saw a horse wearing a decorated saddle.

The dog asked, 'Are you going for an important competition?'

The dog said, 'I am going to the battle-field.'

The dog said, 'You are going to fight the enemy and you could lose your life. Stay back and we will enjoy.'

The horse said, 'If I die, I shall die fulfilling my duty. I will protect my country and thus leave the memory of a good name behind.'

The dog was impressed with his bravery and sacrifice.

Moral: Always fight bravely for the right cause.

Bad Deeds are always Punished

A notorious robber was taken to court. The judge asked, 'Why did you rob so many people?'

The robber replied, 'If I've committed a crime, it is God's will.'

The judge said, 'All right. But give me all your gold or I'll get your head chopped.'

When the robber gave the gold, the judge said, 'You will be killed now.'

The robber shouted, 'I gave you gold to save my life not to kill me.'

The judge replied, 'It was God's will that I lie. Now, I'll take your gold and get you killed. Why blame me?'

Moral: It is wrong to steal.

The Cruel Wolf

Once, a wolf killed a wise bear. The wolf bribed the animals not to speak against him.

However, everyone went to the meeting. When the lion asked, 'Who saw the wolf kill the bear?'

The deer said, 'The wolf snatched honey from the bear and ran away.'

The hawk said, 'When the bear ran to take the honey back, the wolf threw him on the ground.'

'I saw the wolf kill the bear,' said the sparrow.

The lion shouted, 'Since there are so many witnesses, I order that the wolf be punished severely.'

Moral: Cruel people do not have any friends.

71

The Hermit and the Thief

A wise hermit was known for his kindness. One day, a thief stole jewels from a house. While escaping, he accidentally dropped the loot in front of the hermitage.

The villagers marched the hermit to the King. The hermit cried that he had not stolen the jewels. But the King ordered, 'Tie him to a tree.' The next day, the villagers caught the real thief. The King ordered the hermit to be freed and asked his forgiveness.

The hermit said, 'I forgive you. You were only doing your duty.'

The King punished the thief.

Moral: Honest people are always respected.

MAY 2
Stealing is a Sin

Once, a scholar said to his students, 'Whoever steals and brings gold and silver ornaments to me will marry my beautiful daughter.'

All the boys wanted to marry the beautiful girl. So, they set off.

However, one of the boys did not go and said, 'Sir, stealing is a sin. I can't commit a sin just to marry the girl I desire. If this angers you, I will leave.'

The scholar said, 'I had decided to test you all. You alone have proven to be worthy of her.'

The boy and scholar's daughter were married.

Moral: An honest man is always rewarded.

MAY 3
The King and the Wise Man

A king invited a wise man to his palace. He was extremely impressed by the wise man's conduct and said, 'My palace will be blessed if you start living here.'

The wise man replied, 'A true hermit must live in nature. I have nothing to do with royalty.'

The King said, 'Sir, before you leave, ask for anything you want. I shall not refuse it.'

The wise man replied, 'I have all I need. You are a king. Rule well and be a just king.'

The King always did his duty well.

Moral: Do not be too greedy for material things.

MAY 4

Nice People Always Get Help

A lion killed a deer and was eating it.

Just then, a thief passed through the forest. He said, 'Dear lion! I am hungry. Why don't you share this food with me?'

The lion replied, 'I will not share with you. You always steal things that do not belong to you.' Hearing this, the thief went away. Then a traveller walked through the forest and tended to an injured bird.

The lion said, 'Come and share this food with me.' The traveller took the deer. The lion took his share to his den.

Moral: No one likes to help dishonest people.

MAY 5

The Monk and the Tree Spirit

A monk went to a forest. He lit a lamp and offered flowers and incense to the spirit residing in the tree.

The spirit, disguised as an old man, asked the monk, 'Why do you worship this tree?'

The monk replied, 'I want to start a school for needy children. I am praying to the tree spirit as I need money.'

The tree spirit said, 'Your devotion will be rewarded.'

Then, it gave the monk a treasure that was buried under the tree.

The monk's school soon opened and flourished.

Moral: If your intention is good, God will always help you.

The Foolish Sparrows

A flock of sparrows lived in a farmyard.

One day, a kite came to the farmyard and searched for food.

The sparrows said to each other, 'We must do something, otherwise the kite it will eat us.'

So, the oldest sparrow asked a hawk, who lived close by, 'A kite is trying to kill all the sparrows. Please help us by killing the kite.'

The hawk agreed.

The next day, the hawk easily killed the kite. The sparrows' happiness did not last long. The hawk started killing the sparrows for food.

Moral: If you hurt someone, you will be hurt, too.

The King who Hated Old People

A King disliked old people. After ordering his parents to leave his kingdom, he declared, 'All the old must leave the kingdom.'

Out of fear, the people followed the King's orders.

Without the experience and wisdom of the elderly people, things started going wrong.

The fairy queen disguised herself as an old woman. The king saw her and said, 'You are old. You can't live here!'

The old woman smiled and the king suddenly became old. 'We will leave together,' she said.

'All the old people must return,' said the king realising his mistake.

Moral: Show kindness and compassion towards the old.

MAY 8
A Partridge's Sorrow

A hunter trained a partridge to attract and kill other birds. The sad partridge vowed to keep quiet.

However, the angry hunter hit on its head and the partridge cried out in pain. Many birds flew towards it and were captured.

One day, the hunter felt thirsty and went to the monk's house. With its master asleep, the partridge asked the monk, 'Is it my mistake that birds die?'

The monk said, 'You never intended to get the poor birds killed. So, you are not guilty.' The happy partridge flew away from there.

Moral: Do not force others to commit crimes.

MAY 9
Lion's Friendship with the Jackal

A lion fell into wet mud and was stuck. A jackal pulled him out.

The lion was so grateful that he invited the jackal and his family to live near his cave.

One day, the lioness thought, 'What if the jackal and his family harm the lion?'

She frightened the jackal's family. They were about to leave when the lion stopped them. Then he told the lioness, 'A friend can be small or weak. Do not hurt or frighten the jackal or his family again!'

The lioness never troubled the jackal family again.

Moral: Friendship does not see size or power.

Don't Set Bad Examples

A monkey once lived with the humans. He learnt to live and dress like humans.

One day, the monkey went to the forest. When his brothers saw him, they were impressed with his dress and manners.

The monkey said, 'If you all want to look like me then follow what I tell you to do.'

Then he told them about the bad habits of the humans.

The other monkeys happily followed that monkey. They started hurting their closest friends and started lying.

An old Monkey stopped them and said, 'Learn only good habits from others.'

Moral: Do not teach bad habits to others.

The Priest's Son

A royal priest used to arrange for an 'Annual Festival' in a kingdom.

When he died, the ministers said, 'Majesty, the priest's Son is young and does not know anything. He cannot conduct the Festival.'

The son begged, 'The Festival is weeks away, Majesty. I will study hard and become capable. Please give me two weeks time.'

The King agreed.

After two weeks, the priest's son went to the King and said, 'Majesty, allow me to arrange the Festival as I have the skills.'

The King allowed him to arrange the Festival and he did really well.

Moral: No one is too young to perform big tasks.

MAY 12

Be Humble

In a garden, a rose bush was planted close to a dull spruce.

One June, as the rose bush was in full bloom, she looked down on the spruce and said, 'I am the queen of the garden. All the other plants should honour me!'

The rose asked the gardener to cut the spruce.

'The spruce flowers in winter when not a single rose can be seen! She covers and protects you from the cold,' said the gardener.

He added, 'Enjoy your beauty till it lasts. Be kind and friendly towards others.'

Moral: We should be humble and kind to everyone.

MAY 13

The Tortoise and the King

A lazy King and his minister, once, came across a tortoise.
The King asked, 'Tortoise, you are very slow. How will you escape in a fire?'

The tortoise replied, 'I will hide in a hole.'

Then, the minister asked, 'What if you don't find any holes?'

The tortoise replied, 'Then I'll die!'

The King said, 'This foolish creature is ready to die, but won't stop being lazy.'

The minister replied, 'Likewise, a ruler's laziness will also affect his kingdom.'

The King understood what his wise minister meant. He worked hard and became a powerful king.

Moral: We must not be lazy.

Use your Time Wisely

While digging in a mine, the workmen found a huge toad.

They said, 'This toad must be as old as the mountain itself.'

The toad swelled with pride and said, 'There is no one more important than me.'

A fly heard this and said, 'Do not boast! I was born this morning and die this evening. But, I will do everything I need to do in these twelve hours. I will even have children before sunset. It is better to have a short and happy life than a long and wasted one!'

Moral: Make good use of your time.

Don't Trust Strangers

Ellie was a rich but foolish girl. She would blindly trust strangers.

Once, she visited a new coffee shop. Ellie decided to buy it and asked a man, 'Excuse me! I want to buy this shop. Where can I find the owner?'

The man said, 'I am the owner. Give me hundred gold coins and the shop is yours.'

Then, he took the money and went away.

Ellie said, 'Waiters, I am the new owner of this shop.'

A lady said, 'But this shop is mine!'

Ellie was careful with strangers from that day on.

Moral: Strangers must not be trusted.

The Wise Man's Justice

There were four wicked ministers in a King's court. They were unjust and took bribes.

Everyone was troubled by them, but could not openly complain to the King. Then, some people met a wise man and asked for his help.

The wise man spoke to the King, 'Majesty, you need to check your ministers. They are unjust and wicked.'

When the King enquired about his ministers, he realised that the wise man was right. So, he banished the ministers and appointed the wise man as his chief justice.

The wise man did his duty well.

Moral: Always be fair and just.

Revenge Brings no Good

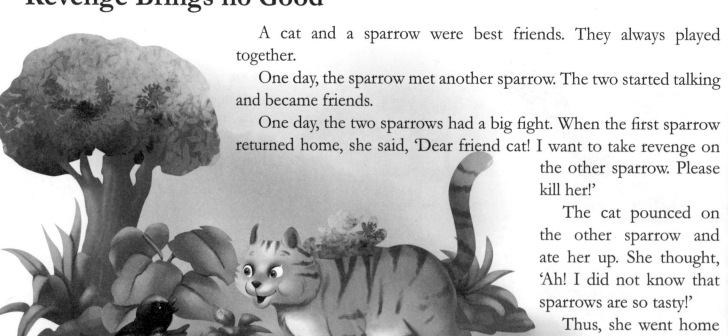

A cat and a sparrow were best friends. They always played together.

One day, the sparrow met another sparrow. The two started talking and became friends.

One day, the two sparrows had a big fight. When the first sparrow returned home, she said, 'Dear friend cat! I want to take revenge on the other sparrow. Please kill her!'

The cat pounced on the other sparrow and ate her up. She thought, 'Ah! I did not know that sparrows are so tasty!'

Thus, she went home and ate her friend sparrow, too.

Moral: Don't be revengeful but learn to forgive.

MAY 18
Clever Moe

Moe was educated but unemployed. He decided to wait for the King at the palace gate and ask for a job.

While waiting, Moe counted the people who went in through the palace gate.

When the King came out for a walk, Moe said, 'Majesty, I waited all day to see you. In the meantime, I noticed that out of ten strangers that went in, only nine came out.'

The soldiers found the stranger hiding in the King's chamber, ready to kill him.

The grateful King appointed Moe as an army commander.

Moral: Observe more than just looking at things.

MAY 19
Anna and Beth

Pretty Anna only made friends with pretty children.

One day, Anna and her friends went for a school picnic and enjoyed themselves.

One of her classmates, Beth asked, 'Will you play with me?'

Anna said, 'I don't like to talk to ugly people like you.' Beth felt very bad but kept quiet. After sometime, she heard a loud shriek. She saw that Anna had fallen in the lake and was drowning.

Beth jumped into the lake and saved Anna's life.

Anna was very ashamed. She apologised to Beth and they became friends.

Moral: A good heart is better than good looks.

MAY 20
Good Company

A King was fond of his elephant.

Once, for two weeks, every night, the elephant heard thieves talking behind his shed. He grew violent.

The King asked for his minister's help.

That night, the minister stayed near the shed. He heard the conversation of the thieves and ordered, 'Post two soldiers near the shed. From tomorrow, the priests will speak of good values outside the elephant's shed.'

The elephant heard only about goodness and kindness. He became calm and friendly again.

The minister said, 'It is important for us to keep good company.'

Moral: One learns good things from good company.

MAY 21
The Big Tree

A monkey, a sparrow and a fox lived near a big tree.

One day, the monkey asked, 'Do you remember how big the tree was when you first saw it?'

The fox said, 'When I was a baby, it was a mere bush.'

The monkey said, 'When I was very young, I had to stretch my neck to reach its topmost leaves.'

The sparrow said, 'I carried the seeds of a great tree here. That was the origin of this tree. So, I have known it since its birth.'

The others respected the sparrow even more.

Moral: Do not judge anyone by their size as each one has their own value.

The Two Best Friends

Lily and Rose lived in an orphanage. They were best friends.

One day, two different families adopted them. So, they started living in two different towns. The girls exchanged pendants and promised to find each other when they grew up.

Lily's parents loved her a lot. But Rose's parents made her do all the chores. Many years passed.

Once, Rose was selling vegetables in the market.

Suddenly, a beautiful girl stopped by. She stared at Rose's pendant and said, 'Rose, I am Lily, your friend.'

Rose was very happy. Lily hugged her and took her home.

Moral: True friendship never fades.

Encouraging Words Always Pay

Once, an elephant trainer trained the King's elephant well.

The King thought, 'This elephant will win every battle for me!'

He challenged the neighbouring ruler to a battle.

With the King on his back, the elephant entered the battlefield. He saw wounded soldiers and scary weapons and ran away.

The trainer encouraged, 'Brave elephant! You are the most powerful creature! Win the battle and make your King proud!'

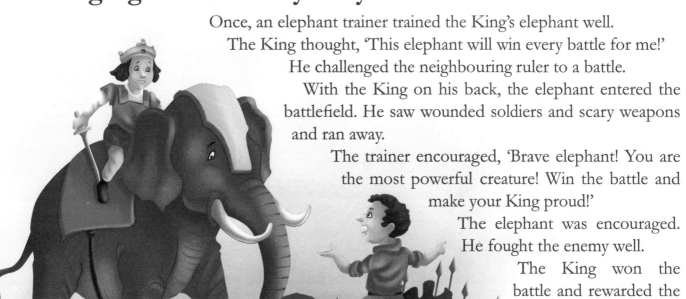

The elephant was encouraged. He fought the enemy well.

The King won the battle and rewarded the trainer for encouraging the elephant.

Moral: A right word used at the right time always helps.

Be Yourself

Once, a music concert was held in the forest. All the birds took part in it. They came and sang their songs. When it was the mockingbird's chance to sing, he started imitating the other birds.

All the birds were angry. They did not like the mockingbird imitating them.

A wren said, 'Mockingbird! You can sing beautifully. All the birds in the forest want to listen to your song. Please sing a new song for us.'

The mockingbird tried but he could not sing a song of his own. He felt embarrassed and flew away.

Moral: Do not copy others.

The Farmer and his Son

A farmer's father passed away. He was so sad, he stopped eating or drinking or working in his fields.

His son, Mike thought, 'I must make father forget his grief.'

He sat beside a dead cow and started crying. Then, he stopped eating and working.

The farmer said, 'Your crying and not working will not bring the dead cow back!'

Mike replied, 'If you think my actions are useless, then why are you crying over someone who is gone?'

The farmer realised his mistake. He began to eat and work again.

Moral: There is no use crying over spilt milk.

Don't Trust Flatterers

A clever rat lived in a hole with other rats.

One day, the rat was hungry and peeped to see if it was safe outside. But he saw a cat waiting outside the hole.

The clever rat said to another rat, 'I want to have the honour of your famous company.'

'Lead the way,' said the other rat.

The rat said, 'How could I possibly go before such a famous rat?'

The other rat was flattered and went out of the hole. The cat carried him away, immediately.

The rat went out happily.

Moral: We must not trust flattery or flatterers.

The Water-Demon's Question

Three princes were hunting in the forest. The youngest prince went for a drink in a lake when a water-demon appeared and asked, 'Who is truly good?'

He said, 'The sun and the moon.'

The answer was wrong! So the water-demon pulled him inside the pool.

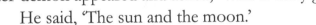

When the second prince came, the water-demon asked the same question. His reply was wrong, so he was pulled inside the pool, too.

To the water-demon's question, the eldest prince replied, 'He who does no wrong is truly good!' This was correct!

The water-demon, happily, released his two brothers.

Moral: Use your common sense.

The Hawk and the Nightingale

A hawk spotted a nightingale and caught her.

The nightingale pleaded, 'Why do you want to eat me? I am so small. You will still be hungry.'

The hawk said, 'I am hungry and have not eaten for days.'

The nightingale said, 'Why don't you hunt for bigger birds?'

The hawk said, 'Do you think I am foolish that I will let go of you to catch something that I can't even see now? I will first eat you and then hunt for more food.'

He ate the nightingale.

Moral: Look for a way out rather than pleading with the wicked.

The Wicked Minister and the Cart Driver

Once, a wicked minister had to halt his horse-cart as another cart had blocked the road.

Enraged by the delay, the minister threw a stick at the cart driver. Strangely, the stick hit the cart, bounced back and hit the minister on his head.

The angry minister complained to the King that the cart driver attacked him.

But the King's chief advisor protested, 'A just King should not imprison the cart driver without hearing his side of the story.'

The King learnt that the minister alone was to be blamed. He punished him.

Moral: Listen to both sides of the story.

The Moon and the Witch

Once, an ugly witch lived near a forest.

All the trees, birds and animals trembled when she entered the forest. The fairies were upset to see them scared. So, they sent the moon to talk to the witch.

The moon asked, 'Why do you scare everyone?'

She replied, 'I don't intend to scare anyone. I come to the forest to befriend animals as I don't have any friends.'

The moon felt sorry and said, 'I understand that you are very kind but the animals are scared of your ugly looks.'

He told everyone in the forest about the good witch.

Soon, all the animals and birds became good friends with the witch.

Moral: Don't judge a person by his looks.

The Foolish Bird

A beautiful Singing Bird lived in a cage. When the other birds were asleep, she sang throughout the night.

One night, a Bat asked, 'Why do you only sing at night?'

The Bird replied, 'I am in this cage because I sang during the day. A bird-catcher heard me and caught me. So, I only sing at night.'

The Bat said, 'If you had done this before you may be free today. Your beautiful voice should be heard in the day by people who are awake. Now, you disturb everyone at night!'

Moral: There is no use thinking of the past.

The Ungrateful Lion

A woodpecker saw a lion choking as a bone got stuck in his throat.

The woodpecker said, 'I can take out the bone. But, you will eat me.'

The lion promised not to eat him. But, the woodpecker fixed a stick between the lion's jaws and removed the bone.

Next day, the woodpecker said, 'Lion, please give some meat as reward for my help.'

The lion growled, 'I left you alive! That was reward enough!'

The woodpecker thought, 'Thank God, I put the stick in his mouth or he would have eaten me!'

Moral: Thank people who help you.

The Talkative King

A King was very talkative.

One day, the King was walking in his garden with his chief advisor. Suddenly, a young cuckoo fell dead at the King's feet.

The wise advisor said, 'Majesty, a crow mistook an egg for its own. However, when it hatched and cried out, the crow understood that it was not a young crow. So, the crow pecked at it till it died and he pushed it out of the nest. Whoever speaks too much, human or bird, suffers the same fate.'

The King took care not to speak more than required.

Moral: Silence is golden.

The Monkey and the Crocodile

A monkey lived on a tree near a river. A crocodile couple wanted to eat the monkey's heart.

Once, the husband said to the monkey, 'Climb up on my back. I'll take you to a place where there are tasty berries.'

The monkey agreed. Soon, the crocodile dived into the water saying, 'My wife wants to eat your heart.'

The clever monkey said, 'But I have left my heart on the tree! Let's bring it.'

When the husband swam back to the bank, the clever monkey jumped off and climbed his tree.

Moral: A witty mind always saves one from danger.

You Reap What You Sow

One day, a cruel King went for hunting in the forest.

The King saw a wolf chase a fox. The wolf bit the fox, but the fox managed to escape.

Soon, he saw a hunter shoot the same wolf.

Within minutes, the hunter's horse stepped over his foot and lamed him forever.

The King realised that they were all punished for doing bad to others. He prayed, 'Dear God! Please forgive me for being cruel.'

The King went back and apologised to his people. He became a kind and loving King.

Moral: Do good and others will do good for you.

The Hunter is Tricked

A hunter followed a fox to her house. He dug a pit, covered it with twigs and put a piece of meat on it.

Then, he hid behind a tree and waited.

After some time, the fox came out and saw the piece of meat. She thought, 'This looks like trouble. I will not eat it.'

She went back in her house.

Later, a tiger saw the piece of meat. He leapt and fell inside the pit. The hunter heard the noise and jumped inside the pit.

The tiger at once killed him and ate him.

Moral: Look before you leap.

The Clever Friends

Once, a little Rabbit lived in an underground burrow. He had seen a sly Fox many times, waiting for him to come out as he could not enter the burrow through the small hole.

One day, the Rabbit saw the Fox chatting with the Weasel. The Rabbit thought, 'Their friendship cannot possibly bring me any harm.' But he was wrong.

Soon the Weasel entered his burrow and attacked the Rabbit. The Rabbit had to run out of the burrow to save himself from the Weasel. But the Fox, waiting outside, immediately pounced on him.

Moral: We should always be cautious.

Wise Saul

Joe went on a journey. He met some wicked goblins who said, 'Don't carry water! There is a lake ahead!'

Joe ordered his men to throw away jars. Later, the thirsty men found no water! While they slept, goblins ate them.

Joe's friend Saul met goblins too on his journey.

Not believing them, Saul said, 'Men, preserve water and use it wisely. Keep your spears handy!'

Saul saw Joe's abandoned carts and took them. His men were armed so, the goblins did not attack.

Saul earned great profits by selling his goods.

Moral: Wisdom and presence of mind helps during problems.

The Priest's Son

A priest's son wanted to become a hermit and pray all day long. But his parents wanted him to marry and have a family.

One day, he made a girl's image in gold and said, 'I will only marry a girl like her, who is pure and calm.'

The priest searched everywhere for the girl. Finally, in a village, the people said, 'This looks just like the headman's daughter. She prays to God all day long.'

The priest's son married the girl and they both lived happily ever after.

Moral: People who think alike can be very happy together.

JUNE 9

The Boastful Prince

A boastful prince once told his friends, 'Tomorrow, I shall go to the forest and hunt a bear.'

His friends said, 'Let's see what he does!'

The next day, as they walked through the forest, the prince asked a woodcutter, 'Have you seen the footprints of a bear?'

'Yes,' said the woodcutter, 'I will take you to its den.'

The prince went pale with fear. 'That won't be necessary!' he stammered. 'I am looking for tracks, not for the bear itself!'

The prince's friends realised that he had been lying about her bravery.

Moral: Boasting does not save you from difficulties.

JUNE 10

The Chameleon

Once, a man said, 'The chameleon is green as I saw it sitting on a tree yesterday.'

His friend said, 'I know the chameleon is blue for I saw it under the clear blue sky.'

The third friend said, 'Don't fight. I caught a black chameleon last night.'

He came back with the chameleon in a white paper box. The three friends were shocked because it was white!

The chameleon said, 'God has blessed me with the power to change the colour of my body according to the surroundings and protect myself from my enemies.'

Moral: Do not believe in rumours.

The Wise Courtier

A King had cruel horse called 'Big Chestnut.'

Once, some horse dealers came to trade.

As their prices were high, the cunning King instructed, 'Let Big Chestnut run loose. He will wound their horses, forcing them to lower their prices.'

A wise courtier suggested the dealers, 'The next time, bring your cruellest horse.' And so it was done.

The King again let Big Chestnut loose. When the horses met, they started licking each other.

The courtier explained, 'Majesty, they will not fight as they are similar. Don't harm other men's goods.'

The King became fair in his dealings.

Moral: Be fair and do not fool others.

The Stag and the Fawn

Once, a deer brought her son to a Stag and said, 'My fawn does not know how to keep himself safe from hunters. Can you teach him?'

The stag agreed.

But the fawn was very overconfident and thought it was boring and useless to learn, so he never went to the stag.

Two months later, the fawn was caught in a trap.

His mother complained, 'Stag, why did you not teach my son?'

The stag said, 'Your son was irresponsible and overconfident. He never came to me.'

The fawn was trapped because he had no time to learn what was useful for him.

Moral: Overconfidence brings trouble.

The Thief and the Neem Tree

Once, a thief put his stolen goods under a neem tree's trunk and lay down.

The neem tree thought, 'If this thief is caught, he will be punished. I will be hurt, too, so, let me drive him away.'

He said, 'Thief, the King's men are coming to get you.'

The thief fled to the forest nearby.

Seeing this, a bo tree said, 'By helping the thief, you have caused trouble to many people.'

The neem tree realised his mistake.

Soon, some soldiers came by. The neem tree informed them about the thief and they caught him.

Moral: It is a crime to help a criminal.

Education is Important

A great King wanted to send his son to a good school.

However, the son pleaded, 'Father, I do not want to leave the comfortable life.'

The King replied, 'Son, you must be well-educated. It will help you to rule the kingdom well.'

Unwillingly, the son left.

Five years later, the enemies attacked. The son was well trained. So, he fought and defeated the enemies.

The King said, 'Son, never misunderstand your parents. All parents take decisions for their children's good.'

The son apologised to his father for mistaking his motive.

Moral: Education and learning helps a man throughout his life.

Hamish's House

Once, Hamish decided to build a house for himself. His friends said, 'Hamish's house would be the envy of all.'

After some months, Hamish's house was ready. Everybody gathered to see how the new house looked.

The house was very small in size. It did not have many rooms or a large garden.

Hamish's friends said, 'This looks like a store room! There is no space outside, too, to grow plants.'

Hamish replied, 'I created this house for myself and not for you. In fact, if you were my true friends, you all would have not been so critical.'

Moral: True friends are better than many friends.

Quality Matters, Not Quantity

Once, the people of a kingdom started quarrelling about their children. They said, 'Whoever has the most children is the most superior!'

A woman said, 'Let us go to our King and ask him.'

They asked, 'Majesty! Please tell us, who among us has the most number of children? That person will be superior-most in the kingdom.'

The wise King said, 'I have only one daughter. She is a kind, honest and a well-mannered child. Indeed, I am very proud of her.'

The people realised their mistake and stopped fighting.

Moral: It is better to have a good child than many bad children.

96

JUNE 17
Dead Mouse Brought Luck

A man could read signs and predict future.

One day, he saw a dead mouse lying on the road. He said, 'Whoever picks up this dead mouse will soon start a business and marry a beautiful girl.'

Young John overheard him. So, he picked up the dead mouse and sold it to a lady for her cat. With the money, he bought molasses, which he sold to a gardener.

Thus, whatever work John did, he was always given a better reward.

Soon, John set-up a business and married a beautiful girl. They lived happily.

Moral: It is not good luck but enterprise and hard work that always pays

JUNE 18
No Job is Bad

Once, a witch owned a broomstick. She used to fly everywhere on it and also used it to sweep her house.

One day, the broomstick said, 'I have such a bad job. Every day, I carefully carry you around. Yet, you use me to sweep the floor. I think I should have a higher job.'

The witch smiled and started cleaning her chimney with the broom. The broomstick started to complain again. The witch said, 'Instead of complaining, you should do your work well. No job is good or bad, as long as it is done properly!'

The broomstick finally stopped complaining.

Moral: Love what you do.

JUNE 19

The Wicked Gardener

An old man had an orchard. When he died, his wicked gardener built a house in the orchard and declared it was his.

The fairies in the orchard decided to teach him a lesson. They caused a strong wind to blow down all the fruits!

The angry gardener shouted at four travellers who were passing by, 'You spoiled my orchard!'

He picked up a stick to beat them. However, being stronger than him, these travellers beat him very badly. Then, they carried him to the King's court.

The King made enquiries and jailed the gardener for cheating!

Moral: Cheating and dishonesty are grave crimes.

JUNE 20

A Mother's Love

A mother goose used to feed her young ones by the pond. She did not allow any other animal to drink from the pond, thinking they might harm her babies.

The goose drove away the ducks, chicken and cat.

One day, a big, strong dog came to drink. The mother goose pecked him and slapped him with her feathers.

The furious dog said to the goose, 'Neither are you strong nor you have sharp teeth. But, I won't say anything to you because you are only protecting your children.'

He drank water and went away.

Moral: One must be sympathetic towards other's situation.

The Kind King and the Fairies

A wise King ruled a country. There were constant droughts in his kingdom; crops failed and cattle died. Many people suffered without food and water.

A sorcerer suggested, 'We must offer some animals.'

The King did not agree as he was against the killing of animals.

The ogres heard this and were displeased. They hid in the King's bedroom to kill him. However, the fairies drove the ogres away.

Hearing the noise, the King woke up. The fairies said, 'Kind King, from now there will never be a shortage of food and water.'

Moral: It is wrong to kill innocent animals.

The Teacher and the Farmer

A teacher and a farmer went on a voyage. A storm broke out and the ship sunk. They escaped by clinging to a plank and floated to an island.

The farmer found food and they ate well.

Soon, a giant appeared and said, 'I am the keeper of this island. You cannot stay here without answering my questions!'

The teacher requested him to return after two days. In that time, he taught the farmer everything he knew.

When the giant returned, he asked them questions and was satisfied with their knowledge. He changed into a boat and took them home safely.

Moral: Share your knowledge with others.

The Corn and the Thresher

Once, a sheaf of corn was being thrashed by the thresher.

The corn said to the thresher, 'Nature has covered me with a nice green leaf. Humans like me because I am their food, then why do they treat me so badly?'

The thresher said, 'Your seeds are eaten by humans. It is only when you are thrashed that your seeds come out. If you are not thrashed then your seeds aren't discovered.'

The corn realised that he was considered useful only after being thrashed. He never complained about being thrashed or beaten again.

Moral: One must not complain as difficulties have hidden blessings.

The Hermit and the Princess

A King prayed as his kingdom was facing severe drought. People and cattle were dying.

The angels appeared in his dream and said, 'A powerful man with magical powers lived on the mountains. Send your daughter there. If he marries her, then he will come to the city.'

The princess agreed. She met the man and impressed him with her beauty and intelligence. He married her and travelled back to the palace.

He prayed sincerely for many days, and soon, it started raining. The King thanked the man.

The princess and the man lived happily.

Moral: Help others with your talents.

The True Friend

A prince and the priest's son were best friends.

When the prince was crowned King, he made his friend a commander. However, the priest son refused the post and went away to lead a monk's life.

Years later, the King fell ill. When the monk heard, he went to the palace.

The King asked, 'It has been so many years. How are you?'

The monk replied, 'I will always be there for you.'

Soon, by the power of his meditation, he healed the King.

The King thanked him and seeked his counsel always.

Moral: A true friend always helps during problems.

Path of Goodness and Truth

A school teacher had lost his young son. He was very sad. His student said, 'Teacher, in my house, no one has died young.'

The teacher was amazed. He was curious to know more and went to the young boy's house. He met the boy's father and asked, 'What is the reason behind your family's long life?'

The boy's father said, 'We follow the path of goodness and believe that whatever happens, happens for a reason. Therefore, we are always happy and blessed with a long life.'

The teacher learnt a valuable lesson and taught good always.

Moral: Doing good has its own blessings.

The Old Man's Treasure

An old man thought, 'After my death, my wife might spend all the money.'

So, he took his treasure to the forest and buried it. He said to his servant, 'Reveal this place only to my son.'

Soon, he died.

The wife said, 'My son, go with the servant and bring the hidden treasure.'

But the servant started abusing the son in the forest.

Disturbed, the son went to a wise man. He said, 'The place where the servant abused is the place where the treasure is buried. Just dig there.'

The son found the treasure.

Moral: Cheaters are always caught.

The Fisherman and the Fish

A fish was training her babies how to swim.

Suddenly, a fisherman lowered his net and the fish was caught. He built a fire to cook the fish.

The fish said, 'I'm not afraid of dying. But my babies won't know their mother.'

The fisherman's wife heard what the fish said. Being a mother herself, she felt sorry and convinced her husband to put the fish back in the water.

The next day, when the fisherman pulled up his net, it was loaded with pearls. The fish said, 'I can give you pearls for your kindness.'

The fisherman started trading in pearls.

Moral: Be kind and understanding towards everyone.

The Man and his Daughters

A good man had two daughters. Claire took care of the crops and Marie did pottery.

One day, the man asked Claire, 'How is your work?'

She said, 'I hope that it rains as the crops need water!'

But Marie said, 'I pray for dry weather to harden the pots!' The man prayed sincerely for his daughters as they wanted opposite things.

Suddenly, the angel of kindness appeared and said, 'Your intentions are good. Don't be sad!'

The next morning, his daughters said, 'Father! It rained in the fields! But, there was bright sunshine over the pots! Our work went on very well!!'

Moral: If we wish well for all, only good things will happen.

The Proud Spring

Two springs of water fell out of the fountain on a hill. One spring flowed slowly, while the other rushed noisily.

The fast spring said proudly, 'Sister, if you flow so slowly, you may become dry. Look at me, people will use me to travel. Ships will sail wherever I flow, then I shall empty myself into the ocean.'

Her sister calmly flowed down where many small brooks joined her along the way.

But as luck has it, the fast spring joined her sister who had now become a river. She was ashamed and apologised for her pride.

Moral: Do not be too proud of your abilities.

The Hunter and the Fowls

A hunter hunted in a forest where many wild animals lived. So, when he came home safe, he would thank God by eating a fowl.

One night, he dreamt that he lived in a country ruled by fowls. They had organised a feast to thank God.

The fowls had actually planned to kill him and serve him at the feast. He shouted, 'Please don't kill me!'

The fowls replied, 'We are thanking God for protecting us!'

The frightened hunter woke up and never killed any animal or bird again.

Moral: Treat others as you expect them to treat you.

The Ant and the Grasshopper

One winter's day, the ants were drying the grain they had collected over the past few days.

A hungry grasshopper saw them.

He said to the ants, 'Have pity on me. Please give me some food.'

One ant said, 'Why don't you store food in summer? That way you would have had plenty during the winters.'

The grasshopper replied, 'Oh, I was so busy singing that I had no time.'

The ant said, 'If you were silly enough to sing all summer, you should now dance, without any food all winter!'

Moral: The grasshopper went away sadly.

The Bird and the Monkey

A bird had built a strong nest to live in.

It rained heavily. A monkey swung to a branch near the bird's nest.

The kind bird asked, 'Why don't you build a shelter to protect yourself?'

But the monkey thought, 'She is well sheltered, so she is teasing me.'

Angrily, he leapt to catch the bird. But the branch broke and he fell down.

The bird said, 'I was just trying to help you. Now that you attacked me, I will not let you shelter under my tree.'

He pecked and chased the monkey away.

Moral: Think twice before you react.

The Clever Wolf

A wolf and a lion were searching for food.

Suddenly, the wolf heard some sheep bleating and said, 'Majesty, I will get some food.'

Then, the wolf saw that the shepherds and their dogs were guarding the sheep. He thought, 'I will not be able to kill them now!' He returned without any sheep.

The lion asked angrily, 'Where is my food?'

The wolf replied, 'The sheep are very thin now. We should wait for them to become fat and then eat them.'

The lion foolishly believed him and decided to leave the place.

Moral: Quick thinking can help during troubles.

The Tribal Princes

A tribal king was angry with his two sons for misbehaviour and banished them.

The brothers went to a city where the people hurled stones at them, shouting, 'They look like beggars from a faraway land.'

The younger brother said, 'The fools don't know that we are princes!'

However, the elder brother explained, 'We are not princes anymore. Stay calm.'

The brothers worked and lived like commoners.

The tribal king had them secretly watched. After three years, he took them back, convinced that they had learnt their lessons in life.

Moral: Parents always have the best interests for their children.

The Wise Bird

Once, a very wise bird lived on a giant tree and preached all day. The other birds became irritated and stopped paying attention to his teachings.

One day, a strong wind blew. The wise bird thought, 'If the tree's branches keep rubbing against each other, they will certainly produce fire and the tree will burn down.'

He told his fears to his companions. However, they said, 'You are an old and foolish bird.'

But the wise bird flew away. In a short while, a fire broke out. The foolish birds couldn't escape the flames and died.

Moral: Pay heed to warnings.

The King and the Wise Man

A wise king was tired with the endless duties and work. He decided to give up his kingdom and become a hermit.

The ministers said, 'Who will rule us? The prince is just a baby!'

The king said, 'All of you can help the Queen till he comes of age.'

The ministers met the kingdom's wisest man. He said to the king, 'You are leaving simply because you are tired. This is not the right behaviour for a king. What will your son learn from you?'

The king realised his mistake and decided not to go.

Moral: Do not run from responsibilities.

The Robin who Loved Music

A robin was fond of music. She flew to a new place every day and sang a new song there.

One day, the robin went to a new country. There, she settled on a tree and began singing her song.

A sparrow who lived on the same tree, did not like the robin's voice.

She said, 'Robin! You should not sing, when the nightingale and the blackbird are more melodious.'

The robin replied, 'I may not have a good voice, but I sing because I love music.'

Moral: You should do what you are capable of, no matter what people say.

The Merchant and the Guide

A merchant was travelling through a hot desert. So, he hired a guide to take him across safely at night.

When the destination was close, the guide said, 'Throw away the wood and water.'

At night, the guide fell asleep and the camels turned back. They were exactly where they were a night before!

'Oh, we were hasty in throwing away our wood and water!' the merchant cried.

Then, he saw some grass which grew only near water. He dug a hole and found water!

The guide thanked the wise merchant.

Moral: Don't act without thinking as everything has its own value.

The Hermit and His Student

An old hermit had an obedient student named Sawyer.

One day, he visited the King who said, 'Hermit, as you are old now, you must stay here.'

A few days later, the hermit began missing Sawyer. Alone, he became depressed, stopped eating and soon fell ill. In spite of his best efforts, the King could not cure him. He took the hermit to meet Sawyer.

On seeing Sawyer, the hermit ate food and grew healthy again. He said, 'Sawyer respects and takes care of me selflessly.'

The King went back alone to his palace.

Moral: True affection can do what medicines cannot.

The Ugly Prince

A brave prince was ugly, so, no one wanted to marry him.

So, he made a golden statue of a girl and said, 'I will marry anyone like her.'

The King's men found a princess who resembled the statue.

But, the King said, 'She will see the prince's face only after marriage.'

She married the prince, but she went back to her kingdom after seeing his face. But, her kingdom was attacked.

The brave prince drove the enemies away. The princess fell in love with him and they lived happily.

Moral: A man should be judged by his deeds not looks.

The Quails and the Hunter

A hunter threw a net over a flock of quails and caught them.

So, the quails went to a wise quail, Mo. He said, 'When the hunter throws his net, fly with all your might; land on a thorn-bush. I will come to rescue you.'

The quails followed Mo's advice. As they landed on the thorn bush, the net became entangled.

When Mo came to help, a few quails started fighting.

Mo flew away, sensing trouble.

The hunter cut the net with his knife and caught the quails.

Moral: If there is no unity among ourselves, we will land in trouble.

The Kangaroo and the Grasshopper

A famous scientist was travelling in Australia and saw a kangaroo. He asked his local guide, 'Do you have wide meadows in Australia?'

'No, about the same size as in England and America,' the guide answered.

Then, the scientist said, 'Are the hay stalks here as long as fifty feet?'

The surprised guide said, 'No, only a foot or two long.' The scientist said, 'It is strange that the Australian grasshopper is so huge!'

The guide replied, 'You saw a kangaroo, not a grasshopper!'

The scientist realised that he still had many new things to learn.

Moral: The learning process never ends.

The Stag and the Doe

One day, a young doe came from the village to graze in the forest. A stag from the forest fell in love with her.

While leaving, the doe cautioned, 'Don't come with me. The village life is filled with dangers.'

However, the stag accompanied her.

Soon, the doe sensed a hunter hiding nearby and let the stag go ahead while she followed him at some distance.

The hunter shot an arrow at the stag. The frightened doe left him and ran away.

The stag was heart-broken. He regretted trusting her and leaving the safe forest.

Moral: Think twice before trusting strangers.

JULY 15

The Boy and his Father

A travelling boy and his father needed a place to stay, and were told that a house was empty but a wicked goblin lived there.

The goblin ate those who never said, 'Long life to you!' Or 'Same to you,' after sneezing.

The goblin raised dust and made the father sneeze. The boy realised this was the goblin's mischief. So, he quickly said, 'Long life to you, father. May that goblin stay away from you!'

The father replied, 'Same to you. May you live long!'

Now, the Goblin could not eat them.

Moral: Quick and clever thinking help in grave situations.

JULY 16
The Bet

Once, a friend asked Lance, 'Do you believe it is possible to drink up the sea?'

Lance replied, 'Yes, it is very easy. I can bet I can do it.'

The next morning, Lance met Mike and told him about the bet. Clever Mike gave him an idea.

Lance asked the friend to come to the sea-shore. Then, he said, 'The bet is to drink up the sea. I said nothing of the rivers that flow into it. Stop them first and I will fulfil my promise.'

The friend went away, accepting his defeat.

Moral: Always make promises that you can keep.

JULY 17
The Kind Villagers

During a severe winter, some monks did not have enough food and warm clothes up in the mountains. So, they set off for the plains. Soon they reached a village where the people were poor.

The kind-hearted and generous villagers put whatever food and other things they could find into a basket.

Handing the basket, the villagers said, 'We are sorry but this is all we have.'

The monks said, 'Your hearts are full of love. Therefore, your gift is most precious. Thank you all!'

The villagers never faced any hardships thereafter.

Moral: Help the poor as much as you can.

JULY 18
The Gardener and the Deer

A deer visited a king's garden often.

One day, the king said, 'Gardener, catch the deer.'

The gardener put some honey on the grass. The deer loved it and became friendly.

Then, the gardener dropped the honey grass on the path to the palace. The deer greedily followed till it entered the palace.

When it heard the door shut, it panicked and began to run about.

The king felt sorry and said, 'Let it go, for it trusted the gardener, who betrayed it!'

The palace door was opened and the deer ran away.

Moral: Do not betray people who trust you.

JULY 19
The Prince and the King

Once, a wise prince disagreed with the King's judgment on a case. The King ordered him to stay away from the court.

The prince was very hurt.

Taking this as an opportunity, some ministers pretended to be the prince's well-wishers and said, 'Your father does not respect you. You must punish him for insulting you. Poison him. Then, you can be the King.'

The prince reported the ministers to the King. He banished them from the palace and promised never to insult the Prince.

Moral: A son will never kill his father as blood is always thicker.

Anger Only Causes Trouble

A wise King and his wife were travelling and stopped to have their lunch in a garden.

The King of that kingdom was also there. When he saw them, he thought, 'These people are not from here. Let me see what happens if I trouble them.'

The King picked up a fruit from the wise King's plate but the wise King merely smiled. The King was annoyed and asked, 'Why aren't you angry?'

The wise King said, 'Sire, we would have fought over nothing, had I become angry.'

The King understood and apologised.

Moral: One should always stay calm and think before acting!

The Scholars and the Foolish Man

A group of scholars recited the holy verses. People would listen to them and even ask them for advice.

A foolish man also bought a book of verses and tried to learn them. He thought, 'If I recite these verses, then I will also be famous and wise.'

Then, he went to the scholars. They said, 'Come to the city square tomorrow.'

Next day, the foolish man started reciting. Halfway through, he forgot and blushed deeply, and fell silent.

An old scholar started reciting the verses. The foolish man realised that he should have not boasted.

Moral: Think before you act.

The King and the Monk

A wicked King was in a garden with his royal dancers. While they danced, the King fell asleep.

The dancers saw a monk meditating under a tree and requested, 'O wise one! Give us some useful knowledge.'

The monk began preaching.

When the King woke up, he was very angry. He shouted, 'You pretend to be a monk. I will teach you a lesson!'

He ordered his soldiers to kill the monk. As he gave these orders, the earth opened and he tumbled inside. Thus, the King was punished for acting unjustly.

Moral: Do not react without knowing the entire truth.

The Hound and the Housedog

A man took his hound whenever he went hunting. Meanwhile, his housedog had to watch his house.

The man always gave a large portion of food to the housedog.

The upset hound said, 'I work so hard to search for food. You don't do any work yet the Man gives you a big share!'

The housedog replied, 'It's not my fault. Rather, it is the man's mistake as he did not teach me how to work hard.'

The hound realised that the housedog will never be able to provide for himself.

Moral: One should be taught to take care of oneself.

The Hermit and the Elephant

A hermit had an elephant as a pet.

His leader warned, 'When elephants grow up they even kill those who care for them. Don't keep it with you for long.'

The stubborn hermit said, 'The elephant is my friend. I can't live without it.'

One day, the hermit had to go very far to get food and returned after a week.

Meanwhile, the hungry elephant became violent. As soon as it saw his master, the elephant caught him in his trunk and threw him on the ground. Then he charged into the forest.

Moral: Listen to good advice and keep good company.

The Wise Elephant

A wicked lion was the king of the forest. He made all the other animals work hard for him. The animals went to the wise elephant and said, 'The lion is mean and makes us do all his work. How do we get rid of him?'

The elephant said, 'I will help you only if you are united.'

Then the elephant went to the lion and said, 'A true king helps his subjects. But you only harm the animals. You must leave.'

Seeing that all the animals were united, the wicked lion became scared and ran away.

Moral: Anything is possible if we are united.

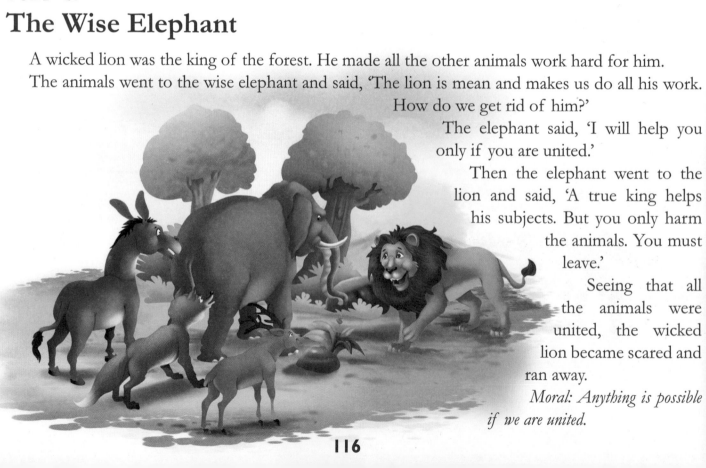

116

The King and his Brother

Once, an elder prince refused to be the new King. So, the younger prince was crowned King.

Some cunning ministers wrongly advised him. So, the King sent his soldiers to imprison his brother.

But his brother managed to escape.

Soon, the enemies attacked. The elder brother disguised himself and joined the army as an archer. He was such a good archer that the enemy was scared and ran away.

The King said, 'Archer, ask for whatever you want!'

The brother said, 'My younger brother's love and trust!'

The King recognised his brother and apologised for his bad behaviour.

Moral: Always believe in your family.

The Young Fox and his Father

Once, a young fox and his father went to a farm at night and attacked the hens.

After a while, father fox wanted to leave with some hens. However, his son said, 'I want to enjoy my treat now!'

The greedy young fox ate so much that he could not breathe. Soon, he died because of over eating!

The sad father fox returned home. But he had a good meal of the hens for a few days. Then, he planned to visit the same farm again.

However, the farmer was ready with his gun and shot him.

Moral: Those who are greedy and steal always have a bad end.

The Man's Two Sons

A man had two sons, Neil and Nathan. Sadly, he met with an accident and lost his eyes.

Neil said, 'Now father is our responsibility.'

Nathan replied, 'We should leave him in an old age home.'

However, Neil took great care of his father.

Few months later, the man said, 'Neil, there is a box full of gold in the bedroom.'

Nathan asked, 'Father, you are giving all your gold to Neil? Am I not your son?'

The man replied, 'Neil took care while you left me to die.'

Nathan realised his mistake and apologised.

Moral: Take care of your parents always.

Name on the Hoof

A fox and a wolf saw a horse and planned to attack it.

The fox said, 'Sir, may I know your name?'

The horse said, 'My name is written on my hoofs.'

The clever fox suspected something wrong. He said, 'My parents were poor. Hence, I never learned to read. The wolf here can both read and write. He is such a bright animal.'

The wolf was pleased with the sweet talk. He at once went to look at the horse's hoofs. When he bent, the horse kicked and galloped off.

Moral: Do not get carried away by sweet talk.

The Student and his Teacher

A teacher taught quickly.

His students often requested, 'Sir, please teach us at a slower pace.'

But the teacher paid no heed and continued in the quick way.

One day, a student began filling water in a pot with a hole at its bottom.

The teacher said, 'It is useless to fill this pot as it cannot retain any water.'

The student explained, 'Similarly, it is useless to teach quickly as your students are not able to retain it.'

Realising his mistake, the teacher changed his method of teaching.

Moral: A teacher has to be efficient as he moulds his students' lives.

The Donkey's Mistake

A travelling merchant unloaded the goods from his donkey's back and draped a lion skin over its back.

Then, he turned the donkey free in the village fields.

The villagers ran away seeing the lion and the donkey ate happily.

This went on till one day the donkey saw another donkey and brayed to get her attention.

The other donkey came closer and so did a curious villager. He shouted, 'It's a donkey! Bring your sticks!'

The angry villagers beat the donkey very hard. The merchant thought, 'Oh, if it had been quiet, it would be alive.'

Moral: Silence is golden.

119

The People who had Never Seen Birds

Many centuries ago, people in a kingdom had never seen birds.

One day, a few merchants from a far away land came there with a crow.

People requested, 'Please sell this bird to us.' And they treated the crow royally.

Then, the merchants brought a Nightingale. She sang beautifully and was loved more than the crow. Seeing this, the crow complained.

The people said, 'She has more talent than you, so we spend more time with her. But we don't keep you hungry!'

The crow understood and became good friendly with the nightingale.

Moral: Everyone has their own place in life.

Little Moon and the Goats

The farmer's bulls, Big Moon and Little Moon pulled carts and were given green grass to eat.

One day, the farmer ordered, 'All the goats in the farm should be given lots to eat.'

Little Moon complained, 'All day, we work in the fields. Yet, we are given just grass to eat. These lazy goats do nothing and are being given so much to eat. This is so unfair!'

On the day of a feast, Little Moon saw the farmer's men kill the goats for their meat. Then, he was content with his life.

Moral: Be happy with what you have.

The Crow and the Pigeon

The cook of a King hung straw baskets on the kitchen window-sills for birds to take shelter.

A young pigeon lived there.

One day, a crow thought, 'I must befriend this pigeon to get inside that kitchen easily.'

He said, 'Pigeon, I wish to be your servant and follow you everywhere.' The pigeon agreed and took him to the kitchen window.

The cook saw the crow and knew that the crow was a greedy bird. So, he threw the crow out of the basket. Moreover, he threw the pigeon out, too.

Moral: Don't pay the price of befriending a bad being.

AUGUST 4
The Crow Caws

A man mimicked the crowing of a crow at a show. The audience shouted, 'There is a crow under your cloak.'

He spread his cloak but there was nothing. Another man said, 'I can do this better.'

The next day, everyone clapped for the first man as the previous day. Next, the other man mimicked a crow, too. He had actually hidden a live crow under his cloak.

The crowd cried, 'This man's imitation is much better.'

The other man pulled the crow from his cloak and said, 'This shows how bad judges you are!'

Moral: One should be judged fairly.

AUGUST 5
The King and his Army

A King had just finished fighting a war with the enemy.

The general was paid well, but the soldiers received less money.

Next, the King ordered that his horses be fed. What was left of the horse's food was then given to the donkeys. The donkeys brayed till the King could not bear it.

His advisor said, 'The donkeys worked as hard as the horses, but got tasteless leftover horse food. Like the foot soldiers, who deserved more, but got less.'

The King understood and rewarded everyone on merit, not just rank.

Moral: One's worth and merit should always be recognised.

The Duck King and the Chief Duck

A bird catcher laid a trap to catch a few ducks.

Unfortunately, the duck king was trapped. Seeing all the other ducks flying away, he shouted, 'Someone help me please!'

The chief duck was the duck king's best friend. He pecked on the bird catcher's hand. The wounded bird catcher let go of the trap.

The chief duck tried to open the trap, but could not. The duck king cried, 'Go away! The bird catcher will kill you, too.'

The chief duck replied, 'I will not leave you.'

The bird catcher was touched and released the duck king.

Moral: Friendship is one of the strongest bonds.

The Young Man and the Camel

A young man, lost in a faraway desert, was looking out for some animal to ride. He then saw a camel for the first time. He thought, 'This animal looks scary. He has long legs, curved neck and a big hump.'

The young man approached the camel but it did not hurt him. He said, 'Let me go closer and try and pat him.'

The young man understood that the camel was harmless.

He soon put a bridle in the camel's mouth and rode him across the desert.

Moral: If we need to use something, we should overcome our fear for it.

The Sad Man and the Happy Man

Two very different men were going on a journey together. The sad man always worried about his future but the happy man sang songs.

The sad man said, 'What if I become blind one day; how will I walk?'

So, he closed his eyes and tried to walk like a blind man.

Just then, the happy man found a purse full of gold.

When the sad man opened his eyes, he saw the purse filled with gold in the happy man's hand. The sad man realised his mistake and felt sorry for himself.

Moral: Be positive and live in the present.

The Old Stag's Sons

An old leader stag placed his herd under the care of his two sons, Luke and Boss. He said, 'Sons, take each of your herd to the mountain forests.'

Boss travelled morning and night with his herd. He kept close to the villages. So, many deer were killed.

Luke never came close to the villages and travelled only at night.

Then, Boss came back alone and Luke returned with all his deer alive.

The old stag said, 'Boss, you lost your whole herd. Luke listened and learned from me. He will be the leader after me.'

Moral: Listen to your parents' advice.

The Frog's Trick

A frog lived in a marshy pond. All the other animals on the ground teased, 'Look at his home in the marshy pond. Even sunlight cannot reach inside.'

The frog decided that he would let others know how good his home was. One fine afternoon, he said to the animals, 'Friends! The magical water in this pond can treat all kinds of diseases.'

The clever fox asked, 'How can the pond water treat diseases? You yourself have a spotted body and a not so healthy-looking face.'

The frog's trick was caught. So, he went away ashamed.

Moral: Never trust sweet talkers and flatterers.

The Heron and her Young Ones

A king had a pet heron. She had babies in a nest in the royal garden.

While she was away, the princes were playing with her young ones. They fell off the nest and died. The heron was shocked! She could only think of revenge!

So, she went to a tiger and said, 'I want you to grab the king's sons and kill them.'

The wise tiger said, 'Killing the princes will be a sin. The dead babies won't come back, but you can have more babies!'

The heron realised her mistake and flew far away.

Moral: Taking revenge will only harm us.

AUGUST 12
The Dog Bite

A man stamped on the tail of a dog sleeping on the road. The angry dog bit the man's foot.

The man asked a friend, 'What shall I do to cure this dog bite?'

The friend suggested, 'It is said that you should go back to the dog and make him lick your wound. Only his saliva will heal you!'

The man laughed and said, 'That sounds very foolish! I would just be asking the dog to bite me again!'

Then the man went to a doctor and was cured.

Moral: Someone who has hurt you once, can hurt you again.

AUGUST 13
The Hunter and the Golden Peacock

A queen dreamt of a golden peacock. The king ordered, 'If there is a golden peacock in the kingdom, bring it.'

His men searched everywhere, but never found the peacock.

Few years later, the queen died. The angry king inscribed on a golden plate, 'On a hill is a golden peacock. Whoever eats its flesh, will live forever.'

A hunter read the inscription and caught the golden peacock.

He said, 'If I eat your flesh, I will live forever!' The golden peacock asked, 'How can my dead flesh make anyone live forever?'

The hunter understood that he must not kill innocent creatures and set him free.

Moral: We must not harm innocent animals and birds.

126

The Fox who had a Cold

All animals were scared of a fierce lion.

One day, the lion ordered, 'I want a bear, a monkey and a fox to come to my den.'

First, the bear entered, but he did not bow. The angry lion killed him at once.

The monkey praised, 'Your Majesty's den smells of perfume.'

However, the lion killed him, too.

Finally, the lion asked, 'Fox, do you also smell perfume in my den?'

The fox cleverly replied, 'I am unable to smell anything because I have a cold.'

The lion laughed and let the fox go.

Moral: Quick and clever thinking always helps.

The King who was Scared of Death

A King was very scared of death. He told his barber, 'When you spot the first grey hair on my head, inform me.'

Few years later, the barber saw a grey hair and informed the King. The worried King thought, 'I am about to die!'

This troubled him day and night. He became disinterested in the matters of his state.

His minister disguised himself as an old man and met the King. He said, 'Death comes to all. However, the important thing is how well we live our lives.'

The King thanked him and lived without fear.

Moral: Death is inevitable.

The Tamed Geese and the Fox

Two geese stayed in a farmyard.

One day, the geese decided to swim down the stream. They reached a soft wet land. There was plenty of grass to eat.

Soon, a flock of wild geese came there and they became friends with the tamed geese.

A fox heard the crackling of these geese and went there.

The wild geese saw the fox and started flying. But, the two tamed geese

were always protected by the farmer, thus, they did not know how to fly. The fox jumped on them and ate them.

Moral: We should be strong enough to protect ourselves.

The Hermit and the Monkey

There lived a hermit and his little son on the mountains.

One rainy day, a monkey thought, 'If I can enter the house, I can steal some food!'

It wore some discarded clothes, held a stick in its hand and stood in front of the house.

The hermit's son said, 'Father, there is a hermit outside. Shall I let him in?'

The hermit realised it was the monkey dressed in hermit's clothes! He went out and drove it away with a stick.

Returning, he said, 'Son, look carefully! It was that monkey, not a man!'

Moral: Don't be fooled by outward appearances.

AUGUST 18
The Hen and the Dog

A tired and hungry hen sat outside an old woman's hut.

The woman felt sorry and threw some grains. After this, the hen began to live near the woman's hut. Soon, she became strong and fat.

One day, the hen's friend, the dog came to meet her. He said, 'Can I also stay here?'

The hen replied, 'You can stay, but never enter the woman's hut.'

The dog agreed. But the dog entered the woman's kitchen and stole meat. The woman was very angry and beat him hard with a stick.

Moral: Greedy people lose more than they gain.

AUGUST 19
The Elephant and the Dog

A King had an elephant. A dog would eat the food which fell near the elephant's dish and became his friend.

One day, a man took the dog away. The upset elephant refused to eat.

The King immediately sent his minister. He saw the sad elephant and noted that it was not ill. He asked, 'Has the elephant become friends with anyone?'

He came to know about the dog and reported to the King. The man was asked to bring the dog back.

The dog and the elephant were happy again.

The King rewarded his minister well.

Moral: True friends cannot live without one another.

The Servant and the Beggar's Dog

A servant of the rich person stopped to look at a beggar at the door.

The beggar eagerly waited for the kitchen maid to give him food. He ate first. Then, he divided the remaining food among his three children. At last, he gave his dog a bone with little meat over it.

The servant thought, 'Just like the dog, I get little to eat. My rich master never helps his poor servants who need money. I wish people would understand that poor people and animals need a lot of help.'

Moral: We must always help the needy and the helpless.

A Puppy or a Kitten

A blind man recognised objects and even animals by touching them.

One day, the blind man went to his neighbour's house for a party. The neighbour's friend teased him, 'I can't believe a man like you can recognise an animal by touching it.'

The blind man said, 'You can test me.'

The friend brought a fox's cub and said, 'Is this a puppy or a kitten?'

The blind man touched it and said, 'This is either a wolf 's or a fox's cub.'

The friend praised the blind man.

Moral: Everyone is talented, we should not doubt someone if they lack something.

Mother's Love

Once, an ostrich met a pelican.

The ostrich said in surprise, 'Oh! Why is there blood on your feathers? Are you hurt?'

The pelican said, 'My little babies peck my body. They grow up feeding on my blood until they are big enough.'

The ostrich was shocked!

The ostrich said, 'The chicks that come out of my eggs look after themselves. In fact, mother ostriches never take care of their babies.'

Now, the pelican was shocked. She said, 'Even though bringing up my chicks is difficult and sometimes painful, it is still wonderful.'

Moral: Mothers love to care for their children.

Great King Bruce

Great King Bruce wanted to fight a battle to exhibit his strength.

His ministers advised, 'Send your beautiful daughter to travel the world. If any King wishes to marry her, he will have to fight with you first.'

Bruce readily agreed. However, no King accepted Bruce's daughter.

But King Nathan wanted to marry her. So, Bruce set out with his army at once.

On the way, he went to a monastery and the monks explained, 'One should not fight unnecessary battles and cause bloodshed.'

Bruce understood and married his daughter to Nathan.

Moral: Battles lead to loss of many lives.

AUGUST 24

The Squirrel and the Snake

A squirrel fell asleep on the highest branch of the tree. When she woke up, she saw a large snake between her and the trunk of the tree.

The squirrel thought, 'If I try to run, the snake will kill me and if I jump, I shall fall.'

Suddenly, she thought of impressing the snake.

'I feel you have the qualities of being the King of the future,' said the Squirrel.

The snake said, 'I do not agree with you.'

Then, as soon as the squirrel tried to escape, the cunning snake swallowed her.

Moral: Foolish talk is of no use.

AUGUST 25

The Kind Leader

A King who was fond of eating deer, kept a herd in his garden. He had granted exemption to the leader of the herd.

One day, it was the turn of a pregnant doe. She requested the leader, 'Let me have my baby. Once my baby is born, I will go.'

He said, 'I will go in your place.'

The King's cook heard him.

Later, the King asked the cook, 'Why is the leader deer here today?'

The cook told him the truth.

The King was so moved that he freed all the deer.

Moral: The kind and the selfless are always rewarded.

132

The Ass and the Dog

An ass and a dog had families on a farm.

The dog's puppies were quick and played around all day. The ass's baby grew up to be very dull.

The ass said, 'Alas! My wife is dull and so my child is dull, too.'

The dog said, 'If my puppies are sharp and intelligent, it is not only because of my wife. I have also taught them many tricks. You should not blame your wife completely. You are also responsible for your baby.'

The ass did not blame his wife ever again.

Moral: We should always do our share of work.

The Beggar and the Rich Merchant

One day, a beggar came to a rich merchant's house but he was chased away.

The beggar said, 'You offer sweets to God every day, but keep his men hungry. God will not answer your prayers till you are kind to the hungry.'

The merchant realised his mistake and took the beggar to his house. Then, he offered the beggar delicious food to eat.

The beggar replied, 'You listened to a poor beggar. Soon, God will bless you. He takes care of those who take care of his people.'

The beggar thanked him and left.

Moral: Be kind to the needy.

AUGUST 28
Dingy and the Geese

A king of geese married a crow and a son was born to them. He was a blue-black coloured bird, named Dingy.

The geese king also had two geese sons.

One day, they made Dingy sit on a stick, the ends of which they held between their beaks.

Just then, the king of the city was sitting in a carriage drawn by four horses. Dingy said proudly, 'I am like the king who is being carried by geese.'

His angry geese brothers shouted, 'Dingy, you think that you are better than us? You can go back to your mother.'

Moral: Think before you speak.

AUGUST 29
The Big Fish

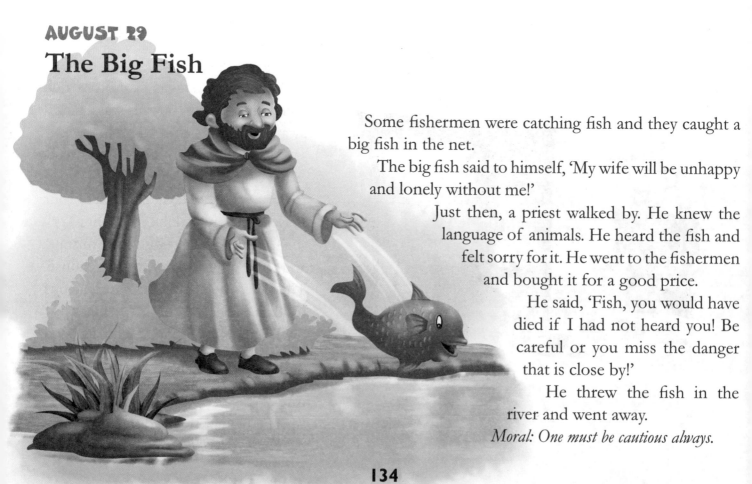

Some fishermen were catching fish and they caught a big fish in the net.

The big fish said to himself, 'My wife will be unhappy and lonely without me!'

Just then, a priest walked by. He knew the language of animals. He heard the fish and felt sorry for it. He went to the fishermen and bought it for a good price.

He said, 'Fish, you would have died if I had not heard you! Be careful or you miss the danger that is close by!'

He threw the fish in the river and went away.

Moral: One must be cautious always.

134

AUGUST 30
The Ungrateful Donkey

There was a well in a city. While people drew water, they also filled up a trough for the animals.

Once, a donkey came to drink water, but the trough was empty. Soon, a man came by. The donkey started neighing angrily and kicked the trough.

The man filled the bucket and said, 'Here, you drink first!'

The donkey drank and then kicked the bucket hard.

The man said, 'I gave you water to drink and you kicked the bucket. I can't drink water now!'

He picked up a stick and beat him.

Moral: Be thankful to those who help you.

AUGUST 31
The Dog's Lessons

It was a hot afternoon. A poor man fainted in the heat. As he lay in the mud, a dog came there.

The dog thought, 'Perhaps this man is searching for food. I shall teach him how to do it properly.'

He said to the man, 'You are wasting your time. Come, I will teach you to smell out food and find it.'

But the man did not even move. The dog said, 'If you had learnt from me, you would have done quite well in life!'

Saying this, the foolish dog went away.

Moral: Don't assume anything on your own.

The Mouse and the Frog

A mouse asked a frog, 'Will you carry me on your back, across the water? I will not bite you. I promise.'

The frog agreed.

When they reached the middle of the stream, the mouse suddenly bit the frog. The frog cried out in pain and started drowning. He asked the mouse, 'You promised not to bite me!'

The mouse replied, 'You stamped my tail once, this was my revenge.'

The frog said, 'Silly mouse. I am dying but you will also sink with me and drown to death.'

Moral: Revenge harms its victim as well as the one who takes it.

The Author and the Labourer

An author saw a labourer hammering stones into a pavement and said, 'My friend, today you are poor and unknown. But, tomorrow you could be famous.'

'I just do my work honestly and get paid for it. Then, I go home and eat a simple meal with my family and sleep peacefully,' replied the labourer.

The author said, 'But, it is important to do big things and become famous.'

'But do you laugh with your family?' the labourer asked.

The author replied sadly, 'I don't get any time for that.'

Moral: A simple, happy life is better than a famous, unhappy one.

The Hare on the Moon

A wise hare preached goodness and kindness to all animals.

Once, the hare looked at the moon and said, 'Tomorrow is a holy day. If any beggar comes, we must offer him food.'

However, the hare realised that he only had grass to offer. So, he thought, 'I shall offer my own self.'

God decided to test him and disguised as a beggar.

Seeing the beggar, the hare built a fire. He was about to jump into it, when God stopped him. He blessed the hare by imprinting his wise form on the moon forever!

Moral: Selflessness is the biggest virtue.

The Wicked Wolf and the Sheep

A pack of shepherd dogs attacked a wolf and left him wounded.

The wolf lay sick in his home, but he was still very wicked.

One day, a sheep passed by the wolf's house. The wolf called, 'Gentle sheep, please fetch me some water from the stream and then I will find some meat to eat.'

The wise sheep knew that the wolf was playing a trick on her.

She replied, 'Oh yes wolf, I know what your plan is. If I would bring you water, you would most definitely make me your meal.'

Moral: Wickedness can easily be seen through.

The Westerly Wind Fails

One day, the sun told the westerly wind, 'No matter how much you blow, I will always be stronger than you.'

Suddenly, the westerly wind said, 'Here goes a man on earth. Whoever succeeds in making him take off his warm clothes will win.'

The sun agreed.

The westerly wind thought, 'I shall force the man's clothes to fly away.'

The man tightened his coat around himself.

The sun thought, 'I shall persuade this man to take off his coat.'

The man began to feel very hot. He quickly took his warm garments off.

Moral: Persuasion is better than force.

The Hermit Made Peace

A lion and a tiger lived peacefully in the same cave at the foot of a mountain. A hermit also lived there.

One day, the tiger said, 'It is always cold at night, which means that night causes cold.'

The lion said, 'It is cold only during the daytime, which means that the day causes cold.'

Their talk turned into an argument.

The wise hermit said, 'Cold is caused by the wind that could blow anytime. Which means that both of you are right.'

Thus, the hermit made peace between the two friends.

Moral: Silly fights could break the closest friends.

SEPTEMBER 7
The Clever Quail

A small quail was picking up food from the forest floor, when a falcon caught him in his claws.

The quail spoke, 'If I was on my old ground, I would have been safe. I wanted to live and die there, like my forefathers.'

The falcon said, 'You can go there. You cannot escape from me even from there.'

The quail flew back and perched on a stone in the ploughed field. Just as the falcon dived, the quail moved aside. The falcon fell with full force upon the stone and hit his head.

Moral: Use your common sense in trouble.

SEPTEMBER 8
The Milkmaid's Dreams

A milkmaid was carrying a pail of milk to the farmhouse and started day-dreaming.

'When I sell this milk, I will buy three hundred eggs,' she thought, 'they will produce around two hundred chickens.'

The woman continued, 'When I sell the chicks, I will buy a new gown! Then, I will go to parties wearing it. A rich man will ask my hand in marriage. But I will toss my head and refuse.'

At that moment, she tossed her head and the pail fell down. All her dreams vanished!

Moral: Don't waste precious time in daydreaming!

SEPTEMBER 9
The Clever Young Monkey

Some monkeys went to the village orchard at night, and started gobbling as much fruit as they could grab!

But a young monkey fell asleep on a tree.

The guard saw them and shouted till the villagers arrived. They lit small fires beneath the trees.

In the meantime, the young monkey woke up.

The clever monkey took a burning branch from under a tree, ran to the village gate and lit a fire near it. Soon, the fence was burning! The villagers ran to put out this fire.

Thus, all the monkeys escaped.

Moral: Quick thinking can save us from troubles.

SEPTEMBER 10
A Good Deed

A traveller was once going to another town to sell toys.

In the afternoon, the traveller found a well and drank some water.

He lay down on the wall around the well. As he was tired he quickly fell asleep.

Just then, a man came by. He woke up the traveller and said, 'Please wake up or you will fall into the well.'

The traveller woke up and said, 'Thank you for saving my life.'

The man said, 'Last year, I too fell asleep on the well's wall. But someone kind saved my life.'

Moral: Always pass on the good deed.

Find Your Own Truth

A King wanted to know what 'truth' was. He asked everyone, but received no satisfactory answer.

Some people told the King's minister about a wise man. When the minister asked the wise man, he replied, 'My son is planting in the field. He'll answer your question.'

The seven year old boy said, 'My truth is that I am planting vegetables so that we have food to eat. What is yours?'

The minister realised that each man must search for his own truth. He told the King this and praised the wise young boy.

Moral: Wisdom has nothing to do with age.

The Poor Potter

A poor potter made an idol of Mercury, the Greek God of work and profit.

He prayed and made offerings of flowers regularly. Despite this, he did not become rich. In fact, he became poor day-by-day.

The angry potter banged the idol against the wall one day. The head of the idol broke from the body and from the broken head came out a stream of gold coins.

The surprised potter said, 'When I cried, you did not listen. But, now when I stopped believing in you, you helped me so much.'

Moral: No matter what happens, we must always have faith in God.

SEPTEMBER 13
The Mighty Bull

A peasant found a calf and cared for him till he became a mighty bull.

One day, the bull thought, 'The peasant has cared for me all his life. I must repay him.'

So, he said, 'Go to the market and boast that your bull can pull a hundred loaded carts. Find a rich man and bet with him.'

The peasant did as the bull said.

The rich merchant bet on this.

The mighty bull pulled the hundred carts till they moved. The merchant paid hundred gold coins to the peasant.

Moral: Be loyal and faithful to those who help you.

SEPTEMBER 14
The Rich Man's Neighbour

A rich man bought a beautiful house. But he did not know that a tanner was his neighbour. A tanner is a person who makes leather from the skin of animals.

The smell that came from the tanner's house was so bad that the rich man found it very difficult to live there.

One day, the rich man requested, 'Tanner, could you please stay in another place?'

The tanner promised but he did not go anywhere.

Finally, the rich man became used to the bad smell, he did not complain any more.

Moral: Life is such that we compromise with it.

The Clever Horseman

A hunter trapped a hare in the forest and was returning home.

On his way, the hunter met a horseman. He said, 'Please give me the hare and I will give you money for it.'

The hunter thought, 'If I sell the hare, I will get money for it. I can always go back and get another hare.'

The hunter gave the hare to the horseman.

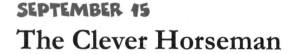

As soon as the horseman took the hare, he rode away without giving the hunter any money.

The hunter chased as fast as he could, but the horseman went further away.

Moral: Do not trust strangers.

The Wise Dog

One night, it rained and the palace dogs chewed the wet leather seats of a King's carriage.

The angry King ordered that all the dogs in the kingdom be killed! The frightened dogs ran to a wise dog and requested, 'Help us or we will all be killed!'

The wise dog met the King and said, 'Your Majesty, it is the palace dogs who damaged your carriage. Feed them buttermilk and grass. I will prove it.'

The palace dogs were fed buttermilk and grass. Strangely, they vomited bits of leather!

The King apologised to the wise dog.

Moral: Always judge fairly.

SEPTEMBER 17
The Ungrateful Travellers

Two tired travellers lay down under the wide spreading branches of a plain tree.

As they rested under its shade, one of the travellers said, 'Don't you think that the plain tree is useless!'

'Why do you say that?' asked the other traveller.

Looking up at the branches of the tree, the first traveller replied, 'It bears no fruit and is thus, of no use to man.'

Hearing the travellers talk, the plain tree said in anger, 'You ungrateful fellows! How can you say that I am useless, while enjoying my shade?'

Moral: Some people do not recognise a true blessing.

SEPTEMBER 18
The Soldier and his Wig

A soldier did not like his bald head and was ashamed of it. So, he bought a black curly wig from the market. One day, the soldier wore his wig before going to for his usual round.

Suddenly, a strong wind blew off the soldier's wig. His friends started laughing. At first, the soldier felt very embarrassed but soon he joined them. He said, 'The wig did not stay with the man from whose hair it was made so why will it stay with me?'

Moral: One needs courage and good spirit to laugh at one's ownself.

The Scholar and his Student

A scholar taught the holy books. One of his students was a boy who knew all the verses by heart.

When the boy grew up, household and business duties took up all his time.

The boy met the scholar and said, 'Sir, I have no time to read and have forgotten everything you taught me.'

The scholar said, 'Son, the holy books are full of wisdom. They will keep your mind clear.'

The boy read the holy books for an hour every morning. He became a better businessman and his family flourished.

Moral: Always remember the good things you have learnt.

The Fortune Teller

On one side of the market, a fortune teller was busy telling people what would happen to them.

Suddenly, a man came running to him. The man said, 'Fortune teller, somebody broke into your house and stole many goods. Go home at once!'

The fortune teller ran home as fast as he could. He was in such a hurry that he left all his things behind.

One of his neighbours said, 'Dear friend, everyday you tell people about their future but today you could not see your own future?'

Moral: Do your best to shape your future first before advising others.

The Widow and the Young Girls

A widow lived alone with two young girls.

The widow's day started with the crowing of her cock. Just as the cock crowed early in the morning, she woke up her girls.

The girls did not like to get up so early or work all day.

One day, a girl said to the other, 'Oh! Our mother wakes us up because the cock crows. Let us kill the cock!'

So, they killed the cock. But this did not change the widow's habit. She slept early and planned to wake her girls even earlier than always.

Moral: Always think carefully before you act.

The Crab and the Crane

There was a small pond in the forest. One day, a crane said to the fish, 'The water here is low and the heat is intense. I can carry you one at a time to a large pond on the other side of the forest.'

The fish agreed. So, the crane carried them and ate them.

At last, only a crab was left. He guessed the crane's intentions and said, 'I'll come only if you let me ride on your back.'

The crane agreed. The crab grabbed and snipped off his neck!

Moral: The wicked are always punished for their deeds.

147

The Kite and the Snake

A kite was chasing a snake.

By the river, a hermit had bathed and laid out his wet clothes to dry. The snake sat on these clothes.

The kite said, 'Kind hermit, I am hungry. I want to eat that snake sitting on your clothes.'

The hermit replied, 'Kite, I will give you something else to eat. But do not eat this snake.'

The hermit took both of them to his hut. He told them, 'It is best to love and be kind to each other.'

From that day onwards, both the creatures lived with the hermit.

Moral: Peace and harmony solves all problems.

The Wicked Minister

Once, a wise King banished his minister for his misbehaviour.

The minister went to the neighbouring kingdom and impressed the King there. He was quickly made a minister.

The minister thought, 'I can influence this King to attack the wise King.'

However, the King was practical, and called one of his couriers. He said, 'Find out why he was banished.'

After hearing the matter, the King said, 'Minister, a man who does not respect and talks ill about his previous employer should never be trusted. Leave at once!'

The minister was ashamed and went away.

Moral: Respect your employer.

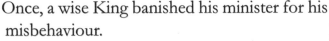

The Woodcutter and the Oak Tree

Once, a woodcutter decided to cut a strong oak tree and make a boat out of it. He chopped the tree with his axe and soon the tree fell to the ground.

He thought, 'If I sharpen the branches from one side I can use them for dividing the oak's trunk into two parts.'

When he used the branches to cut the trunk, the oak cried, 'When the axe hit me, it did not hurt me that much but when now my own branches are tearing me apart it hurts a lot.'

Moral: We are most hurt by those we love.

The Clever Young Rabbit

A young rabbit was caught in a snare. His mother asked his father, 'Have you taught our son all the tricks he needs to know?'

The father said, 'Our son has learnt all the tricks very well. He will be back soon.'

In the meantime, the young rabbit was lying still with his eyes wide open and tongue sticking out, pretending to be dead.

Thinking he was dead, the hunter loosened the trap and started to gather sticks.

The rabbit quietly stood up and hopped swiftly back to his mother.

Moral: Remember all that you have learnt in times of troubles.

SEPTEMBER 27

The Arrogant Son

An arrogant son said to his mother, 'I want to sail on the oceans.'

His sad mother begged him to stay, but he insulted her and left home.

During his sea journey, he landed on an island and went inside a cave.

There sat a man wearing a crown of blades. However, the son thought they were beautiful crown of lotuses and asked for it. But when he placed the crown on his head and felt great pain.

The man said, 'I was unkind to my parents and was cursed to wear this crown of blades. Now you are being punished for being wicked to your mother.'

The man left and the son cried miserably.

Moral: Don't be disrespectful to your parents.

SEPTEMBER 28

The Swallow and the Spendthrift

There was a young man who was a spendthrift. He was popular among his friends as a good spender. So, over time, he wasted his fortune, trying to live up to his reputation and found himself with not even a single penny.

Just then a swallow flew by, chirping merrily. The swallow had appeared before its season. Thinking that summer had come, he went to a clothes dealer and sold off all his winter clothing.

Some days later, a change in weather brought severe cold. The spendthrift suffered miserably without any winter clothes.

Moral: Do not make hasty decisions.

150

SEPTEMBER 29
Truth and the Merchant

A merchant was travelling through a desert and saw someone at a distance.

As he came closer, the merchant could clearly see a woman standing alone. She looked very sad and lonely.

He got off his camel and asked her, 'Who are you?'

After a long silence, the woman replied, 'My name is truth.'

The merchant asked, 'Why are you standing here alone?'

The woman sadly replied, 'Earlier, very few people were liars. Now times have changed and most people are liars, they ignore truth. So, I have left the city and live here alone.'

Moral: Truth often stands alone.

SEPTEMBER 30
The Horse and his Trainer

A King had a favourite horse. He engaged a skilled trainer for him. As the horse imitated and learnt other things from the trainer, it also picked up his habit of limping.

The trainer said, 'Majesty, I have trained your horse as best I could, but it limps!'

A doctor was called but he declared the horse to be fit.

A clever courtier watched a training session. He said, 'Majesty, the horse knows this man is his trainer. He limps, so the horse limps.'

The King got another trainer and the horse stopped limping.

Moral: Bad company brings bad habits.

Strength in Unity

A man had four sons who were always fighting with each other. The man decided to teach them a lesson. He said, 'Bring me a bundle of sticks and try breaking it across your knee.'

All of them failed.

Then the man undid the bundle, and handed them the sticks one by one, which they broke easily.

The man said, 'If you stand united, you will be no match for your enemies. But if you fight and stay away from each other, your weakness will put you at their mercy.'

His sons never fought again.

Moral: United we stand, divided we fall.

The Woodman and his Axe

A woodman accidentally dropped his axe into the river.

He cried, 'Please help me, God. My axe was my only means of living!'

God Mercury appeared from the river and the woodman told him about his axe.

Mercury went back and brought up a golden axe. He asked, 'Is this yours?'

The woodman said, 'No!'

Then, Mercury returned with a silver axe. The woodman refused to take it.

Finally, Mercury brought an iron axe. The woodman said, 'Thank you, this one's mine!'

Mercury pleased with his honesty gave him the golden and silver axes, too.

Moral: Honesty is the best policy.

The Hare and the Tortoise

Once, a hare was boasting of his speed before all animals. He said, 'I have never been beaten. I challenge any one here to race with me.'

A tortoise said, 'I accept your challenge.' So, a race started.

The hare ran, at once, but soon stopped and lay down to have a nap. He thought, 'The tortoise will never be able to catch up.'

The tortoise slowly walked, and when the hare awoke from his nap, he saw the tortoise just near the winning-post and could not run in time to save the race.

Moral: Slow and steady wins the race.

The Lion and the Mouse

A little mouse was running around a sleeping lion. This woke the lion and he angrily placed his paw upon him.

When he opened his big mouth to swallow him, the mouse cried, 'Forgive me, I shall repay your kindness someday.'

The lion was so amused at the idea of the mouse being able to help him that he lifted up his paw and let him go.

A few days later, the lion was caught in a net. The little mouse saw the lion's sad plight and gnawed away the ropes of the net.

Moral: Little friends may prove very useful.

The Valuable Lesson

A man lived with his old ill father and young son.

One day, his neighbour said, 'How long will you take care of your father? Bury him in the cemetery.'

Next morning, the man started digging a pit in the cemetery. His son said, 'What are you doing?'

'We can't take care of your grandfather. So I will bury him,' said the man.

His son said, 'Then I must do the same for you.'

The ashamed man said, 'No, son, I am wrong. I will take care of my father.'

Moral: It is one's duty to take care of his parents.

The Mice's Failed Plan

Once, some mice discussed the best way of saving themselves against the cat.

Many suggestions were made and argued upon.

Then, one mouse stood up and said, 'I have a wonderful suggestion which will take care of our safety. We should tie a bell round the cat's neck. The ringing bell will warn us of her coming.'

Everyone loved the suggestion and clapped for the mouse.

Then an old mouse said, 'I agree that the plan is wonderful, but who is going to bell the cat?'

No one wanted to do that.

Moral: Giving advice is easy but not following it.

The Two Crabs

An old crab and her little son lived near the sea shore.

The old crab had a criticising nature. One day, she said to her little son, 'Dear son, you always walk sideways which looks very ugly. You should walk straight.'

The little crab knew well about his mother's nature and calmly said, 'Show me how dear mother, and I'll follow your example.'

The old crab tried to walk straight but failed every time. She then realised how foolish she had been to find fault in her child. She apologised and never criticised anyone wrongly.

Moral: Set an example before passing instructions.

The Foolish Frog

Two little frogs were playing near a pool when an ox came for a drink. By accident, he trod on one of them.

The mother frog asked the little frog where his brother was. The little frog said, 'An enormous creature came to our pool and trampled him down in the mud.'

The mother replied, 'I too can grow huge and scare him.'

She started puffing herself to look as big as possible. 'Is he as big as this?' she asked.

'Much bigger!' replied the little frog. The mother kept puffing up until she burst!

Moral: Always remember your limitations when you try to compete.

The Treasure and the Farmer's Sons

A dying farmer wanted to tell a secret and called his sons to his bedside.

He said, 'My sons, in my vineyard there is a hidden treasure. Dig and you will find it.'

As soon as their father was dead, the sons took spades and dug up the whole vineyard over and over again, in their search for the treasure which they supposed lay buried there.

But, they found nothing! However, the vines produced a great fruits that year because of the digging. The farmer's sons earned profits and understood what their father meant.

Moral: Hard work reaps true treasures.

OCTOBER 10
The Wolf and the Child's Mother

A hungry wolf was searching for food.

Then, suddenly he heard the cries of a child and came to a cottage. As he went near the window, a mother said to the child, 'Stop crying or I will throw you to the wolf.'

Thinking she really meant what she said, the hungry wolf waited there for a long time.

In the evening, he heard the mother consoling her child, 'If the naughty wolf comes, daddy will kill him.'

The disappointed wolf walked away, saying, 'You can't believe a word they say!'

Moral: Enemies' promises are made to be broken.

OCTOBER 11
The Young Ones

One day, a lioness and a vixen were talking about their young ones. They discussed how healthy and well-grown they were, and what beautiful coats they had, and how they were the image of their parents.

Then, the vixen taunted the lioness, 'My litter of cubs is a joy to see. But I notice you never have more than one.'

The lioness proudly walked away, saying, 'Yes, just look at that beautiful collection of yours! But, what are they going to be? Foxes! I have only one, but remember that one will be a lion.'

Moral: Quality is better than quantity.

The Young Boy and the Man

Once, a young boy was bathing in a river. He went into the deep side and was in great danger of being drowned.

Soon, he started screaming for help.

A man who was passing along the road heard his cries for help. He went to the riverside and began to scold him for being so careless, but made no attempt to help the boy.

The boy cried out loud, 'Sir, please help me first and scold me later.'

The man realised his mistake and helped the boy.

Moral: Give assistance, not advice, in times of crisis.

The Wrestler and the Flea

A wrestler prayed to God Hercules for strength and happiness.

One day, as the wrestler was waiting for the wrestling match to start, a flea bit him.

The wrestler screamed in pain and prayed to Hercules for help.

After a while, the flea bit for a second time.

The wrestler cried, 'Hercules! If you did not help me against a flea, how can I hope for your help against stronger opponents?'

Suddenly, Hercules appeared. He said, 'I will only help you if you do your best to help yourself.'

The wrestler learnt a wise lesson.

Moral: Self help is the best.

The Rich Man and his Servant

A rich man hired a new servant. The servant was good in all the work and his master was pleased but for the dark colour of his skin.

The master thought, 'His former master did not take care of his cleanliness. The colour of his skin is dirt collected over many days.'

So, the master instructed that the servant be scrubbed with hot soapy water.

This went on for many days and the servant was badly bruised. He also got a severe cold, but it still did not change the colour of his skin.

Moral: What is inborn will never change.

The Sailor and the Sea

A sailor left on a long voyage in a calm and pleasant sea.

One day, a storm brew-up in the sea and the sailor's ship drowned.

The sailor swam for many hours and reached an island.

He angrily said to the sea, 'People see you calm and come sailing, but then you raise a storm and leave all the sailors shipwrecked.'

The sea said, 'Sailor, I am always calm like I look but when strong winds come, they raise a storm in me.'

The sailor learnt not to blame people wrongly.

Moral: Our reactions are based on the situations we face.

Unity is Strength

A rich city was attacked by enemies. People were asked to give ideas to safeguard their city.

A bricklayer said, 'We should use bricks to make thick walls.'

A carpenter suggested, 'We can use timber to make our boundary strong.'

These ideas failed because the enemy was very strong.

At last, a currier said, 'I am a poor man who makes leather. There is no material which is as strong as skin. Every man's skin is strong enough to fight the enemy.'

Everyone agreed. They fought together and saved their city.

Moral: No enemy can harm us if we are united.

The Lion and the Prince

A King dreamt that a lion killed the prince and built a lovely palace for him.

The young prince was unhappy to be locked up.

Looking at the painting of a lion, he said, 'Because of you I am shut here. I will beat you.'

He started hitting the painting. Instead he hurt himself.

The Queen bandaged his arm and said to the King, 'Just because of a dream, you are causing so much unhappiness for my son.'

The King understood and let the prince roam freely.

Moral: It is better to face our troubles bravely than to hide from them.

OCTOBER 18
The Wise Fisherman

A fisherman had learnt to fish as a little boy from his father.

One morning, the fisherman made a very good cast and captured a huge number of fish. The net was very heavy and he did not have anybody to help him.

The fisherman thought, 'Now, it is wise to keep all the large fish in the net and take them to the shore. While I do so, the smaller fish will fall back through the meshes of the net into the sea. This is what father taught me, too!'

Moral: In emergency only the important matters should be dealt with.

OCTOBER 19
The Foolish Dog

A dog barked at people and bit them without any reason. He troubled everyone who came to his master's house.

The embarrassed master tied a bell round the dog's neck to warn people of his presence.

The foolish dog grew very proud of his bell.

One day, an old dog said, 'It is better that you don't show off your bell, my friend. Do you think that your bell was given to you as a reward of merit? Rather, it is a badge of disgrace.'

The dog realised his mistake and behaved himself thereafter.

Moral: It is foolishness to believe that what you do is always right.

The Two Pots

A river carried down two pots, one made of earthenware and the other of brass.

As the pots were floating down, the earthen pot said to the brass pot, 'Please stay at a distance from me and do not come close.'

The brass pot replied, 'But why not, we are both friends and are floating in the same direction?'

'If you would even touch me gently, I shall break into pieces, therefore, I do not wish to come anywhere near you,' saying this, the earthen pot moved away.

Moral: It is silly to be friends with someone who can harm us.

The Wicked Man

A wicked man killed another man for money and escaped. He reached the banks of a river. There, he saw a hungry lion. To escape from the lion, he climbed up the tree.

The man had barely climbed the tree, when he saw a poisonous snake, on a tree branch. He thought, 'If I jump into the river, I can escape from the lion and the snake.'

He jumped into the water. There in the water lay waiting a hungry crocodile with his mouth wide open.

The crocodile caught the man and ate him up.

Moral: The wicked are always punished.

The Lion and the Bowman

A skilful bowman went to the forest and challenged, 'Is anyone ready for a game of hunting?'

A lion roared, 'I take up your challenge!'

The bowman said, 'This messenger arrow will teach you a lesson.'

The arrow wounded the lion. Roaring in pain, he backed off from the game.

A fox said, 'This was just the first attack. You cannot run away like a coward?'

The lion roared, 'If the arrow has harmed me so much, imagine the harm the bowman himself would do!'

Moral: If you have accepted a challenge, be on guard from the very first attack itself.

The Man and the Lamp

A man bought a new lamp and lit it. At once, the light brightened the room.

The lamp proudly said to the Man, 'I give out more light than the sun.'

He started burning more brightly.

Just then, the man opened the window. Cold wind blew inside and put out the lamp. The lamp became very sad.

The man said, 'Do not be proud of your light. You should not show off but give light in silence. The sun gives out light to all quietly and it also doesn't need to be relit.'

Moral: One must shine yet be humble like the sun.

The Oak Trees

Once, the oak trees complained to God Jupiter, 'Why do we have to live a life like this? Why do the farmers and the woodcutters chop us down?'

Jupiter said, 'You should be thankful for your lives. Your wood makes excellent pillars and stands. By providing your wood, you are helping them. If they did not chop you, you would be of no use.'

Hearing this, the oak trees realised their value. Since then, the trees do not mind being chopped down.

Moral: Life becomes happier if we think of others and try to help them the best way we can.

The Wise Rose

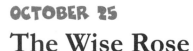

A gardener planted an amaranth tree in a rose garden. One day, the amaranth said to a rose, 'You are a lovely flower. I am sure God and all men like you a lot. I also like you but I envy you your beauty and perfume.'

The rose replied, 'I agree with you that I am liked. But I bloom for a short season. But you live in every season. It is more important to live a meaningful life than just a beautiful one.'

The amaranth understood that the rose was right.

Moral: Inner strength is more valuable than temporary beauty.

The Two Soldiers

Two soldiers were travelling together. Suddenly, they were attacked by a robber. One of the soldiers ran away immediately to hide and left the other to defend himself alone.

The brave soldier fought and struck the robber with his strong right hand.

Just then, the timid soldier drew his sword to strike the fallen robber.

The brave soldier said, 'Put back your sword in the sheath.'

The timid soldier said, 'I have come to help you, my friend.'

'You are not brave and not my friend for I cannot trust you,' said the brave soldier.

Moral: Actions speak more than words.

The Cat's Promise

A cat was in love with a handsome man. So, she prayed, 'Goddess Venus, please change me into a woman.'

Venus said, 'I will but you must forget your cat habits.'

The cat promised and was changed into a woman.

The cat married the man and went to his home as his bride.

But Venus wanted to test if she kept her promise and put a mouse if front of her.

The cat, at once, pounced on the mouse, forgetting that she was a woman now.

Venus was disappointed and changed her back into a cat.

Moral: One's true nature cannot remain hidden for long.

OCTOBER 28

The Boastful Ant

An ant was searching for food when he came across a chrysalis.

The chrysalis moved its tail, and attracted the attention of the ant, who realised that it was alive.

'Poor creature!' mocked the ant. 'While I can run and climb, you lie imprisoned here in your shell!'

But, the chrysalis did not reply.

A few days after, when the ant passed that way again, he saw a beautiful butterfly.

The butterfly said, 'Why don't you pity me now and boast of your powers to run and climb?'

Then, the butterfly rose in the air and flew away.

Moral: Appearances are deceptive.

OCTOBER 29

The Lonely Bat

Once, a great battle took place between the birds and the beasts. When the two armies were collected together, the bat hesitated which army to join.

The birds said, 'Come with us.'

But he said, 'I am a beast.'

When the beasts said, 'Come with us.'

He said, 'I am a bird.'

Fortunately, no battle took place. So, the bat went to the birds but they all turned against him. He then went to the beasts, but he was turned away.

So, the sad bat had to live alone.

Moral: He who supports neither groups nor the other has no friends.

OCTOBER 30
The Ass and the Farmer

A farmer wanted to buy an ass and went to the market. He saw a good ass and asked the owner, 'I want to take him on trial to see what he is like.'

The owner agreed.

At home, he put the ass into a stable along with the other asses. The ass immediately went to the laziest and greediest beast.

When the farmer saw this, he, at once, handed him over to his owner, saying, 'I saw what sort of beast he is from the companion he chose for himself!'

Moral: A man is known by the company he keeps.

OCTOBER 31
The Two Frogs

Two frogs lived in a pond.

One hot summer, the pond dried up. The frogs left to look for another place to live.

On their way, they came across a deep well. One of the frogs looked down into it, and said to the other, 'This looks like a nice cool place. Let us jump in and settle here.'

The other frog was wise and warned, 'Not so fast, my friend. Supposing this well dried up like the pond, how should we get out again?'

The first Frog agreed and they went looking for another place.

Moral: Always think of the consequences.

167

The Crow and the Pitcher

On a hot summer day, a thirsty crow was searching for water. Then, suddenly he saw a pitcher. Hoping to find water there, he flew to it with delight.

But he noticed that the pitcher had very little water and that he could not reach it. He tried everything he could think of, but all his efforts failed.

At last, he collected as many stones as he could carry in his beak and dropped them one by one into the pitcher.

Finally, the water was within his reach and thus saved his life.

Moral: Necessity is the mother of all inventions.

The Ant and the Dove

An ant went to a riverbank to quench its thirst. But, it fell into the river accidently and was carried away by the rushing river.

A dove sitting on a tree saw the drowning ant. She plucked a leaf and dropped it near the Ant.

The thankful ant climbed onto it and floated safely to the bank.

A little later, a hunter took an aim at the dove.

The ant guessed his intention and stung him in the foot. In pain, the hunter threw down his bow, and the noise made the dove fly away.

Moral: One good deed deserves another.

NOVEMBER 3
The Fox and the Grapes

A fox was strolling through a vineyard one hot summer's day. He saw a bunch of ripe grapes on a high branch.

The fox thought, 'This is just the thing I need to quench my thirst.'

Walking a few steps back, he took a run and a jump, and just missed the bunch. Turning round again, he jumped up, but failed.

Again and again he tried to grab the grapes, but at last he had to give it up.

The disappointed fox walked away, saying, 'I am sure they are sour.'

Moral: It is easy to despise what you cannot get.

NOVEMBER 4
The Goose and the Golden Eggs

One morning, a farmer found a yellow glittering egg in his goose's nest. When he picked the egg up, it was heavy.

The angry farmer was about to throw it away, thinking, 'Someone had played a trick on me.' But he took it home and soon found that it was a golden egg.

From then on, every morning, the same thing happened, and he soon became rich by selling his eggs.

As he grew rich he became greedy, 'I must have all the gold at once!'

So, he killed his goose but found nothing inside it.

Moral: Greed can destroy you.

The Fox was Fooled

An ass and a fox were good friends. One day, they went hunting in the forest.

Then suddenly, they saw a lion. The cunning fox went to the lion and whispered, 'Sir, if you promise not to hurt me, I will bring the ass for you to eat.'

When the lion agreed, the fox led the ass to a pit and cheated him to fall in it. The foolish ass fell in the pit.

The wicked lion, seeing that the ass would not escape, at once, pounced on the fox and ate him.

Moral: Never betray your friends.

The Bear's Advice

Two travellers were passing through a forest when suddenly they saw a bear. One of them quickly climbed a tree and hid there.

The other traveller, knowing that bears do not touch a dead body, fell on the ground and pretended to be dead.

The bear smelt him and went away.

When the bear left, the first traveller climbed down the tree and asked, 'Friend, what did the bear whisper in your ear?'

The other traveller taunted, 'He advised me never to travel with a friend who leaves me in times of danger.'

Moral: Misfortune tests the sincerity of friends.

The Fox in a Marsh

A fox was swimming across a river till he was carried away by the current into a deep marsh. The bruised fox was unable to move and lay there while some hungry mosquitoes fed on him.

A passing hedgehog felt sorry and asked, 'Should I drive away the mosquitoes?'

The fox replied. 'No! These are full as they have been feeding for some time. If you drive them away, more hungry ones will come and drink up all the blood I have left.'

The hedgehog could not do anything for the fox and went his way.

Moral: A needy thief steals more than one who already has plenty.

The Frogs and their King

Once, the fogs in a pond requested God Jupiter for a King. Jupiter threw down a huge log of wood into the pond. Soon, the frogs realised that the log was harmless. They climbed up and began jumping on it.

In a short while, the frogs sent another request to Jupiter, 'We are quite upset with such a lifeless ruler. Please send a new King.'

Jupiter was angry with the thankless frogs and sent a crane.

The wicked crane ate the frogs one by one till there were none left.

Moral: No ruler is better than a cruel ruler.

The Stag and the Master

Once, a stag was chased by hunter's hounds. He came to a stable and buried himself in a heap of hay.

Soon, the hunters came and asked, 'Have you seen a stag?'

The stable boys, who had been resting after their dinner, looked around, but could not see anything and the hunters went away.

After a short while, their master came in. He pointed to the heap of hay and said, 'What are those two curious little things sticking out of the hay?'

The stable boys saw the stag and handed him to the hunters.

Moral: Nothing escapes the master's eye.

The Lion and the Bear

A lion and a bear attacked a deer at the same moment, and fought fiercely for it.

They had hurt each other very badly and finally lay down, tired.

A fox was watching the fight for a long time. When he saw them lying on the ground, he grabbed the deer and ran away as fast as he could.

Not being able to run, the lion said to the bear, 'We fought so hard for the deer and the fox stole it!'

Moral: It sometimes happens that one man does all the toil, when he is foolish, another gets the profit.

The Hunter and his Hound

A hunter had a hound who had served him well. But with age he began to lose his ability to hunt.

Once, the hunter saw a deer and set the hound at him.

The hound caught the deer. But with his teeth gone, he could not hold him for long and the deer escaped.

When the hunter scolded him, the Hound said, 'My will is as strong as ever but my body is old and feeble.'

The hunter understood and took him home.

Moral: Honour people for what they had been instead of abusing them for something not in their control.

The Foolish Goat

A fox accidentally fell into a well. He tried different ways to get out of the well but he failed.

After a while, a goat came there.

The fox said, 'Why don't you dive in and quench your thirst?'

When the goat jumped into the well, the fox asked, 'Could you please place your feet on the wall so that I can get out? I will help you get out, too.'

The foolish goat readily agreed. The fox leaped out of the well saying, 'Goat, you did not think before helping me out.'

The poor goat regretted helping the cunning fox.

Moral: Always be cautious of cheaters.

The Proud Horse

A proud war horse met a donkey carrying a heavy load. He said, 'Donkey, you are useless. I have work to do. Move away.'

The poor donkey gave way to the horse.

Soon, the horse was hurt in an accident and his master sold him to a farmer.

One day, the donkey saw the horse drawing a cart full of load. He said, 'Horse, why are you walking so slowly? If you keep walking at this pace, you will never reach your destination.'

The horse apologised to the donkey for his rude behaviour.

Moral: Never be too proud of your work.

The Apple Tree

A peasant had an apple tree in his garden. It bore no fruits, but provided a shelter for the sparrows and grasshoppers. The peasant decided to cut it down.

But the sparrows and the grasshoppers said, 'If you cut the tree, we will have to seek shelter elsewhere.'

The peasant, however, refused to listen to them and cut through the trunk. The tree was hollow inside and contained a swarm of bees and a large store of honey.

Delighted, the peasant threw down his axe, saying, 'The old tree is worth keeping.'

Moral: Old is Gold.

The Footprints

An old lion was no longer able to hunt food for himself. So, he pretended to be sick in his cave.

When the other animals entered his cave to enquire about his health, he ate them.

One day, a fox addressed the lion from outside and asked him how he did. The lion replied, 'I am in a bad shape. But, why do you stand outside? Please come in.'

The clever fox said, 'I would have if I hadn't noticed that all the footprints go inside the cave and none go out.'

Moral: The clever and witty save themselves from difficulties.

Death Came When Called

An old woodcutter cut a bundle of wood from a forest and started carrying them home. He had a long way to go, and was tired much before he reached halfway.

Throwing his burden down, the woodcutter said, 'I wish death would come and release me from this life of work load.'

These words were barely out of his mouth when death stood before him. The frightened woodcutter had enough presence of mind to stammer out, 'I meant the heavy bundle of wood. If you would be so kind, please help me with my burden.'

Death helped him carry the heavy wood to his house and vanished. Thus, the woodcutter cheated death.

Moral: Ask only for what you really want.

NOVEMBER 17

The Swan's Song

A swan knew that if it ever sang it would die.

A man invited his friends to listen to his Swan's song, not being aware of this. But the swan remained silent.

The man was very kind. He did not ill treat the swan.

After many years, the man fell ill. This made the swan so sad that it broke into a sweet, sad song. The man felt so good that he became better.

Sadly, the swan died, saying, 'Master, you were always kind to me, I'm happy that my song could cure you.'

Moral: One should always be grateful.

NOVEMBER 18

The Old Horse

An old horse which carried his rider to battle was sent to work in a mill instead.

He no longer found himself stepping out proudly to the beating of the drums, but was forced to work all day grinding the corn.

One day, the horse said, 'I was once a splendid war horse, attended by a servant. But, how different is my present condition!'

The miller replied, 'It is no use regretting the past. Fortune has many ups and downs. You must just take them as they come.'

Moral: Do not dwell on the past, make the best of today.

The Old Farmer and his Ass

During a war, an old farmer sat in a meadow watching his ass graze.

Then, all of a sudden, he saw some soldiers marching towards them.

The farmer screamed, 'Run or else, we will be captured!'

But the ass just looked round lazily and said, 'Do you think they will make me carry heavier loads than I have to now?'

'No,' said the farmer.

The ass said, 'Then, I don't mind if they do take me, for my life will not be any worse than now.'

Moral: Hard working people will always be the same no matter where they are.

The Mice and their Leaders

Once, there was war between the mice and the weasels.

A meeting was called because many mice were being killed. An old mouse said, 'We have no leaders to plan and direct us in the field. That is why we lose every time.'

A few mice became leaders and wore large helmets. They then led the mice to battle but they were defeated as usual.

Everyone ran home to safety except the leaders. Their helmets were so large that they could not get into their holes, and fell easy victims to the weasels.

Moral: Greatness carries its own penalties.

The Sick Stag and His Friends

A sick old stag gathered a large heap of fodder with great difficulty, thinking, 'This food will last me for the remaining days of my life.'

He lay down on it, nibbling and waiting quietly for his end.

The stag had always been lively during his younger days and had many friends. They came in to see him and helped themselves to the stag's fodder while talking over old times.

The poor stag finally died not because of sickness but because of lack of food which his visiting friends had eaten up.

Moral: Thoughtless friends bring more hurt than profit.

The Cunning Rat

Once, a cunning rat saw a tempting piece of cheese in a trap. He was well aware that if he touched the cheese, he would be caught. So, he thought of an idea.

He went to one of his friends and said slyly, 'I have found a delicious piece of cheese, my friend. I cannot eat it as I just had a hearty meal.'

The innocent friend believed and thanked him. Without thinking, he sprang at the cheese and the trap closed, killing him instantly.

Now, the cunning rat ate the cheese in peace.

Moral: Do not listen to a sweet-talker.

The Fisherman and the Trout

A fisherman stood on a river bank with a fishing rod and bait. He threw his bait so skilfully that a young trout came rushing towards it.

Her mother stopped her, 'Dear child, never be too hasty where there is a possibility of danger. Take time to think, before you take risks. How do you know whether that is really a fly or the snare of an enemy? Let someone else take that chance before you.'

No sooner had she uttered these words that a salmon pounced upon the artificial fly and was captured.

Moral: Do not rush into a strange position.

The Clever Old Mice

A man was troubled by mice in his house. He brought a clever cat home.

The cat ate so many mice that those who were left stayed closely in the upper shelves.

The cat thought, 'Let me hang by my hind legs to a peg in the wall and pretend to be dead. In that way, the mice would no longer be afraid to come near me.'

An old mouse saw through the cat's trick and shouted, 'We will not come near you, even if your skin were stuffed with straw.'

Moral: The old and wise cannot be tricked or taught.

NOVEMBER 25

The Prince and his Monkeys

A prince had trained his pet monkeys to dance. They were great mimics and gradually became great students.

The prince dressed them with rich clothes and masks just before the show. The audience usually clapped repeatedly after each of their grand performances.

Once, a mischievous courtier took a handful of nuts and threw them on the stage.

The monkeys forgot their dancing and fought with each other for the nuts. The embarrassed prince thought, 'I was a fool to think that I could teach them new tricks. Old habits die hard.'

Moral: Do not expect animals to behave like humans.

NOVEMBER 26

The Wicked Eagle

An eagle lived on a tall tree while a fox lived in a hole under the tree.

One day, the eagle took the fox's cub while the fox was out, and feasted on it.

After some days, she saw some people sacrificing a goat on an altar. She suddenly seized a piece of flesh along with a burning cinder and carried it to her nest.

The nest burned along with the chicks and fell at the bottom of the tree. The fox gobbled them up, as the eagle watched.

Moral: Treat others as you expect them to treat you.

The Stork and the Cranes

A farmer had once placed nets on his newly sown fields. The net caught many cranes who had come to eat the seeds.

One day, a stork was trapped and fractured his leg in the net. He pleaded the farmer, 'Please spare me and let me go this time as my leg is hurt. Besides, I am not a crane but a stork.'

The farmer laughed and said, 'You may not be a crane but you were caught stealing with these thieves. Now you will be punished for keeping their company.'

Moral: A person is judged by the company he keeps.

The Four Oxen

Once a lion saw four healthy oxen and his mouth watered. He always prowled about the field where they lived.

The lion tried to attack them many times but they turned their tails to one another, so that whichever way he approached them he was met by the horns of one of them.

One day, the oxen argued about something and started fighting among themselves. They each went off to eat alone in a separate corner of the field. The lion attacked them one by one and soon made an end of all four.

Moral: United we stand, divided we fall.

The Fox and his Friends

Once, a fox lost his tail while escaping from a trap. He was very ashamed but he schemed to convince all the other foxes that being tailless was much more attractive, thus, making up for his own deprivation.

The fox went to his friends and said, 'Cut your tails off. You would not only look better but you will also get rid of the weight of the inconvenient brush.'

But a clever old fox stopped him and said, 'If you had not yourself lost your tail, my friend, you would not advice us to do the same.'

Moral: Misery loves company.

The Horse and the Hunter

A horse and a stag had a terrible fight. So, the horse went to a hunter for help to teach a lesson to the stag.

The hunter agreed, but said, 'Let me place this piece of iron between your jaws and this saddle upon your back.'

The horse agreed. With the help of the hunter, the horse hunted down the stag. Then, he said to the hunter, 'Remove those things from my mouth and back.'

The clever hunter said, 'But I prefer to keep you as you are at present.'

Moral: If you allow men to use you for your own purposes, they will use you for theirs.

The Vulture and the Kind Merchant

A kind merchant helped some vultures during a storm. They said, 'Let's reward the kind merchant.'

Thus, the vultures started dropping precious goods in the merchant's courtyard.

Just then, he came to know that the King had lost many valuables.

The wise merchant understood that the vultures were stealing from the King.

When the vultures' leader was caught and brought to the King's court, he said, 'We were merely repaying the kind merchant.'

The kind merchant said, 'I will return the valuables. Please release the vulture.'

Thus, the King released the vulture.

Moral: Do not commit a crime to repay anyone.

DECEMBER 2

Appreciate What you Have

A pup was sleeping in the garden when he saw a cat on a wall. He thought, 'It must be so nice to be high above the ground. If only I could climb!'

Then, he heard the goldfish in the bowl, wishing, 'It looks so nice and warm on the grass. I wish I could lie down on it!'

A swallow flying by, said, 'I wish I could play the whole day like this dog. I didn't have to search for food.'

The pup realised that he should appreciate what he had.

Moral: The grass is greener on the other side.

DECEMBER 3

The Enchanted Monkey

Once, it was announced in the forest, 'The Bear King wants to find the animal with the best writing. He will be made the minister.'

A mute monkey heard this and began to write beautifully. The Bear King called his daughter, the princess, to see the talented monkey.

However, she had magical powers and said, 'This monkey has been turned mute by an evil witch.'

Luckily, she also knew how to reverse the spell. The young monkey became the minister and served the Bear King faithfully. He remained loyal all his life.

Moral: Repay the kindness of others with loyalty.

185

The Dream Interpreter

The lion king had a wise fox as his minister.

One night, the king dreamt that as he poured water on a tree, a fire came out and burnt all the other trees around.

The fox said, 'This means you would be blessed with a cruel son. But, he could be a noble king only if guided and taught well in childhood.'

Soon, the King was blessed with a boy. He immediately put the fox in charge of his cub's education. The cub ruled the kingdom well.

Moral: Children who are taught good things always grow up to be good adults.

The Snake Charmer Monkey

Danny monkey was a snake charmer. His wife and children did not know about his trade.

One day, his wife asked him to show her what was inside. He replied, 'I can't tell you, for your own safety.'

One night, when Danny was asleep, his wife quietly took the basket outside and opened it. She let out a loud scream when she saw the snakes inside.

Before she could put the lid back on, the snakes slithered into the fields. Poor Danny had to work hard in a field to earn his living.

Moral: Do not hide things from your family members.

DECEMBER 6

Sue, the Wise Pelican

Sue, the pelican, was a skilled doctor. Once, a tigress said, 'Please help my husband! He is very ill, and refuses to leave the cave.'

Sue went with the tigress.

'An owl told my husband he would die soon,' said the tigress. 'My husband is lying in bed, waiting for death.'

Sue struck a match and set fire. Immediately, the tigers ran out of the cave.

'There is nothing wrong with you,' said Sue. 'You believed what the owl said, and thought you must be sick.'

The tiger never believed anyone blindly ever again.

Moral: Do not believe in superstitions.

DECEMBER 7

The Three Monkeys and the Nightingale

Two monkey brothers lived with their younger sister in a forest.

One day, the sister wished for a magical nightingale that lived in a faraway land.

The brothers promised to bring the nightingale. Their friend, an old owl said, 'The nightingale lives on top of the mountain. Do not turn around, no matter what you hear.'

Sadly, the brothers turned when they heard several voices and became stones.

Their sister went after them and refused to look back.

She found the nightingale, who told her how to free her brothers.

Moral: Control and will power often helps us in difficulties.

DECEMBER 8
From Rags to Riches

Alice, the rabbit, was poor but kind.

One day, her neighbour, the otter, needed a coin to mend his fishing net. Alice gave him the only copper coin she had.

The otter thanked Alice and promised, 'I will give you the first batch of fish that is caught today.'

The otter caught a single fish and as promised, he took it to Alice. As she cut it, she found a big diamond inside it.

Alice sold that diamond and bought a new home, started a business and gave some to the otter.

Moral: If you do good, good will come back to you.

DECEMBER 9
Hess, the Selfish Rope Maker

Hess, the elephant, was a rope maker. All he earned every day was just enough to buy food for his family.

One day, a kind boar gave him some money. Hess did not tell his wife about it, as he thought that she would spend it all. He wrapped the coins in an old cloth and hid it in a jar.

The next day, Hess noticed that the jar had disappeared! His wife said, 'I exchanged the jar for an earthen pot.'

Hess told his wife about the coins and apologised for his selfishness.

Moral: A selfish person often loses all.

DECEMBER 10
An Unlucky Bear

A bear found a honeycomb and hid it inside his turban.

Then, he went to the market to buy some meat. Soon, a falcon swept down towards him and tried to snatch the meat from his hand.

The bear waved his other hand fending it away. But the bird persisted in grabbing the meat bag.

Seeing the bear fight a lone battle, a few animals came to his rescue and threw stones at the bird.

The frightened falcon let go of the meat bag, but it grabbed the bear's turban and flew away.

The poor bear lost his favourite food.

Moral: Do not fight for what is not worth it.

DECEMBER 11
Betsy and the Wolf

Betsy, the goat, lived with her kids near a forest. One day, while leaving home, she said, 'Kids, do not open the door to the Wolf.'

Soon, the wolf came and said, 'Open the door, it is your mother.'

The innocent kids opened the door.

The wolf gobbled them up and slept.

When Betsy returned, she saw something moving inside his body. She carefully opened his stomach. Her kids came out, safe and sound!

They quickly filled his stomach up with heavy stones. The wolf's stomach was so heavy that he fell into the lake and drowned.

Moral: Imposters are always punished.

189

DECEMBER 12
The Young Trumpeter

A young trumpeter played great music with his trumpet. Once, an enemy attacked his country. The army head asked him to accompany the soldiers to the battlefield. He readily agreed.

The war was very fierce. But the trumpeter used to play music that boosted the soldiers' courage.

Soon, the war ended. All brave soldiers were rewarded. Even the trumpeter was awarded. A soldier complained, 'He is not a soldier. He only blows a trumpet.'

The senior officer said, 'When our men were sad, he encouraged and guided them in the battlefield. He never gave up!'

Moral: Sometimes words are as powerful as actions.

DECEMBER 13
Clever Enemies

Once, a leopard went to a pool to drink water. Just then, a boar also came there to quench his thirst.

Both of them wanted to drink first. So, they attacked each other with so much anger that they started bleeding.

When they stopped to rest, they saw a large group of vultures, looking at them, longingly.

In no time, they understood that the vultures were waiting for one of them to be killed by the other so that they might feed on his dead body.

So, they became friends and quenched their thirst.

Moral: Do not fight among yourselves.

The Raven who wanted to be a Swan

A raven admired a swan deeply. He thought, 'The swan has such beautiful feathers. I too want to become as beautiful as the swan.'

The raven started thinking of ways to become as white and beautiful as the swan.

Finally, he concluded, 'The swan lives in water all day. That is what actually makes her look so beautiful.'

Then, he left behind his home, his friends and loved ones in search of such waters. But he soon realised that he had given up everything he had for a wish that could not be fulfilled.

Moral: Contentment is the biggest gain.

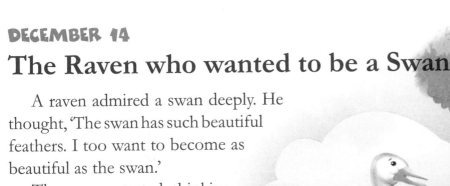

The Dog's Bone

A dog was going home with a bone in his mouth. Before reaching home, he had to cross a small stream.

While walking on the narrow bridge, the dog looked down at the water and saw his reflection. He thought, 'There is another dog with a bone in his mouth!'

He greedily wished he could have the bone in the water too and opened his mouth to grab the bone. But the bone in his mouth fell in the water! The dog realised his mistake and sadly went home.

Moral: The greed of wanting more will make one lose what he has.

DECEMBER 16
Wise Juno

A peacock also tried to sing like a nightingale but he could not.
So, he complained to Goddess Juno.

Juno said, 'You are different than the nightingale. You are much prettier and the colours on the tail feathers are gorgeous.'

The peacock replied, 'But what use is of this beauty, so long as other birds can sing better than me?'

Wise Juno said, 'Everyone is special in some way. You have been given beauty; the eagle has been given strength; and the raven is considered lucky.'

The peacock understood and thanked Goddess Juno.

Moral: You should be satisfied with your qualities.

DECEMBER 17
The Two Goats on the Bridge

Two goats were crossing a small bridge from opposite ends and met at the middle of the bridge. The bridge could let only one goat to cross at a time.

A goat said, 'Why don't you walk back and let me cross the bridge?'

The other goat replied, 'Why don't you move back and let me pass?'

So, the two proud goats argued till they locked their horns and fought dangerously.

Soon, the two of them lost their balance and fell in the stream. They realised that they should have helped each other instead of fighting.

Moral: Sometimes, only comprising helps.

The Bird Catcher is hurt

A bird catcher went to a field to catch birds. He saw a bird sitting on the tree and threw his stick at it. He tried very hard to catch the bird but was unable to reach it. He started jumping up and down. The bird immediately flew away.

The bird catcher was angry and he carelessly hit a viper, who was sleeping by the side of the tree.

The viper at once bit him. The bird catcher now fell down, crying, 'I came here to hunt a bird but I hurt myself.'

Moral: Don't put yourself in danger out of anger and carelessness.

The Young Deer

A young deer was quick and many animals admired her speed.

One day, as the young deer was looking for food, some hunter hounds saw her. They said, 'We should catch her for dinner!'

The hunter hounds chased her for a long time.

The tired deer saw a large cave that belonged to a lion. Without thinking, she went and hid in the cave.

However, the lion in the cave wanted to eat the deer too. So, he hid himself.

When the hunter hounds went away, the lion pounced on the deer from behind.

Moral: Be careful of your safety always.

The Tortoise who Talked Too Much

One year, there was no rain and a drought occurred in a country. So, a tortoise and two geese decided to migrate to a new land.

The tortoise asked the geese to bring a stick and said, 'Hold the two ends of the stick between your beaks. I will grab it in my mouth from the middle. Then, we can fly together.'

The geese warned the tortoise, 'Do not talk when we fly.'

The tortoise agreed and the three flew away.

But the foolish tortoise opened his mouth to talk, he fell to the ground and died.

Moral: Silence is golden.

The Eagle and the Hunter

An eagle was flying around looking for her prey. After hunting for some time, she grew tired and landed on a rock to rest.

A hunter was hiding behind the rock. He saw the eagle and shot an arrow at her.

When the arrow wounded her, the eagle looked at the arrow and saw that it was made of other eagle's feathers. She cried, 'Alas! A hunter whose arrow has my brothers' feathers has wounded me. This is such an irony!'

With great effort, she flew away from there.

Moral: We often give our enemies the means for our own destruction.

The Donkey who Behaved like a Dog

A man had a donkey and a lapdog. The lapdog was his master's pet and lived with him.

But the donkey lived in a stable and had to work hard.

One day, the donkey ran into the house and jumped on the master's lap as he had seen the lapdog do. But his clumsy tricks broke the table and smashed all the dishes on it.

The servants, hearing the noise, ran to help their master. They hit the donkey and kicked him out of the house.

Moral: Be satisfied with what you have, instead of wanting what someone else has.

The Lion and the Woodcutter's Daughter

A lion fell in love with a woodcutter's daughter. He went to the woodcutter's house and said, 'Woodcutter, I want to marry your daughter.'

The frightened woodcutter did not want to marry his daughter to the lion. So he said, 'Yes, but first, cut your sharp teeth and nails, for my daughter is scared of them.'

The lion readily agreed. He had his nails and teeth cut.

The woodcutter saw this, he was no longer afraid. He beat the lion with his stick and drove him back to the forest.

Moral: It is foolish to change into someone that you are not.

DECEMBER 24

The Liar

Once, a dolphin saw a monkey drowning and mistook him to be a man. He placed himself under the monkey and started swimming towards the shore of Athens.

The dolphin asked, 'Are you an Athenian?'

The monkey lied, 'I belong to one of the noblest families there.'

The dolphin then asked about a harbour of Athens, 'Do you know about Piraeus?'

The monkey replied, 'He is my friend.'

The dolphin, at once caught his lies. He removed his support and the monkey drowned.

Moral: Those who pretend to be what they are not, sooner or later, find themselves in deep trouble.

DECEMBER 25

The Cock and the Jewel

A cock searched for grains not only for himself but for all the hens in the farm.

One morning, as the hungry cock was scratching the ground for some grains, he found something that was shining brightly.

'It is a precious jewel,' he exclaimed, 'It must be the farmer's lost jewel! He would be delighted to have found you, but I have no use of you and would have been happy with just a barley corn.'

The cock dropped the jewel back and went looking for some grains of corn.

Moral: Precious things are for those that can value them.

The Fast Hare

A hound was chasing a hare. The frightened hare ran fast.

A shepherd was watching the hound and the hare. He came closer to the hound and called out in a loud voice.

The hound asked, 'Why are you calling me?'

The shepherd was not aware why the hound was chasing the hare. He said, 'The little hare is a better runner than you, hound!'

The hound said, 'You do not see the difference between us. I was only running for my dinner, but the hare is fast because he is running for his life.'

Moral: Necessity is our strongest weapon.

The Unkind Woodcutter

Once, a Fox pleaded to a Woodcutter, 'Please help! The Hunters are after me.'

The Woodcutter hid him in his hut.

The Hunters soon came and asked, 'Woodcutter, have you seen a Fox here?'

The Woodcutter pointed to the hut where the Fox was hiding. The hunters took no notice and left.

When the Woodcutter saw the Fox leave, he said, 'You have not thanked me!'

The Fox replied, 'I would have. But I saw that your thoughts and actions were not as kind as your words.'

Moral: Real help means being true and honest to the person you are helping.

The Mask in the Theatre

Once, a dog entered a theatre. He was hungry and was looking for food.

He saw a man's face staring at him from the stage and said, 'Please sir, could you give me some food?'

The man just stared back without saying a word. The dog went closer, thinking the man had not heard him. But now he saw that the face was not of a man at all! It was just a mask!

The dog said, 'It is good that I found out the truth before I wasted more time talking to it!'

Moral: Things may not always be what they appear at first.

The Cunning Jackdaw

God Jupiter wanted to choose the most beautiful bird and make him the King of all birds.

All the birds wanted to be the most beautiful and become King of all birds.

A jackdaw knew that he was an ugly bird, so he collected the feathers of his friends and stuck them on his body.

'Now I have become the most beautiful,' the jackdaw thought.

God Jupiter chose the jackdaw as the King. All the birds were angry with him. They started pulling out their feathers from his body. The jackdaw became ugly again.

Moral: Don't pretend to be someone else.

The Farmer's Warning

A few birds ate a farmer's crops, after he left the fields.

The farmer decided to scare the birds away with a sling. The frightened birds did not come near the fields. But soon, the birds realised that the sling hanging in the air would not hurt them. They started eating the crops again.

The upset farmer attached stones to the sling and hit the birds.

The other birds left the fields, crying, 'The time has come for us to leave the fields quickly. The farmer is not scaring us but is actually killing us, cruelly.'

Moral: Pay heed to warnings.

The Clever Bat

Once, a bat fell to the ground from a tree. Right then, a weasel tried to eat him.

The bat cried, 'Let me go. I am not a bird but a mere mouse.'

The weasel let the bat go.

After sometime, the bat fell to the ground again.

This time, he was caught by another weasel. When the bat pleaded, the weasel said, 'I hate mice, so I will eat you.'

The bat convinced, 'I am not a mouse, I am a bat.'

The foolish weasel quickly let him go.

Moral: It is wise to turn tricky circumstances to your advantage.